D0363998

THE OBSERVER'S
POCKET   SERIES

.   .   .

THE OBSERVER'S BOOK
OF AIRCRAFT ✍   ✍

The Observer's Books

THE OBSERVER'S BOOK OF

AIRCRAFT

Compiled by
WILLIAM GREEN

With silhouettes by
DENNIS PUNNETT

Describing
ONE HUNDRED AND FIFTY AIRCRAFT
with 272 illustrations

1961 Edition

FREDERICK WARNE & CO. LTD.
LONDON

FREDERICK WARNE & CO. INC.
NEW YORK

Tenth Edition January 1961

Recommended by
THE AIRCRAFT RECOGNITION SOCIETY
THE AIR SCOUTS' DEPARTMENT
of
THE BOY SCOUTS' ASSOCIATION
AIR BRITAIN
REGISTRATION RESEARCH

Printed in Great Britain

INTRODUCTION TO THE 1961 EDITION

The Observer's Book of Aircraft for 1961 is the tenth annual edition of this pocket guide to the world's current civil and military aeroplanes. Now published in the Netherlands, Germany and Switzerland, as well as in the United Kingdom and the U.S.A., the *Observer's Book* has for the past decade —in which more than one-and-a-half million copies have been sold—recorded each year's aeronautical débutantes and the numerous modifications applied to older types in order to improve their performances or widen their operational capabilities. They have been ten years in which both commercial and service aviation have undergone dramatic transformation; transformation that becomes immediately apparent if a comparison be made between the contents of the first annual edition of the *Observer's Book* and this, the tenth edition.

When the 1952 edition was published, the Korean War— a conflict which was to play an important part in the subsequent development of military aircraft—was dragging on, and while such survivors of the Second World War as the Corsair and Invader were re-enacting the tasks in which they achieved fame in the greater conflict, the opposing swept-wing fighters of East and West, the MiG-15 and the F-86 Sabre, were ushering in a new era in aerial combat. But such has been progress in aeronautical development that the reader may find it scarcely credible that, a mere ten years ago, all combat aircraft were subsonic and the bulk of the world's military aircraft were still piston-engined; that the world's first turbojet-driven airliner, the de Havilland Comet, was just entering service; that the helicopter was still looked upon by many as a novel contraption of dubious value, and that the guided air-to-air missile was still very much the pipe dream of the aircraft armament specialist. Yet, surprisingly, the vast majority of the aircraft described and illustrated in the 1952 edition of the *Observer's Book* are still flying today, in one form or another, and quite a number of them, such as the Neptune, the Comet, the Sabre, the Dove, the Heron, the Noratlas, and the Safir, remain *in production*!

The past twelve months have not been singularly noteworthy for the radically new aircraft types to which they have given birth—at least, in so far as those which may be revealed at the time of closing for press are concerned—and few readers are likely to consider them to have formed a vintage year. The year's most radical development, however, had not been revealed as this edition went to the printers. This, Hawker's remarkable P.1127 V./S.T.O.L. strike aircraft, had begun preliminary trials but little could be revealed apart from the fact that it was powered by a

Bristol Siddeley BS 53 lift/thrust ducted fan engine embodying the revolutionary feature of moveable jet nozzles which allow the jet effluxes to be directed downward for lift, backward for thrust, or in any intermediate direction. Other newcomers which did not appear in time for inclusion are Handley Page's H.P.115 narrow delta research aircraft, and the Bristol Type 188 which is intended for research at speeds of the order of Mach 2·5–3·0. Nevertheless, the one hundred and fifty aircraft types described include several notable newcomers to these pages, such as the Avro 748 and Antonov An-24 short- and medium-haul commercial transports, the Rhein RF-1 S.T.O.L. six-seater which features a ducted pusher airscrew, and the Grumman A2F-1 Intruder low-level strike aircraft which employs hinged tailpipes.

Undoubtedly the most notable technical event to take place in the United Kingdom during 1960 was the first transition from normal wing-borne flight to stationary jet-lift hovering and back again by the Short SC.1, Britain's first flat-rising jet-lift aircraft which, accordingly, reappears in this edition after an absence of two years. Possibly the most widely discussed aircraft of the year was, however, the Lockheed U-2 which, recorded in the 1958 edition as a high-altitude research aircraft, was revealed in a more sinister role during 1960 when an aircraft of this type crashed well within the borders of the Soviet Union while undertaking a clandestine reconnaissance mission. Thus, the U-2 also reappears in the pages that follow.

Once again all facts and figures have been checked with meticulous care, and the reader will find that the majority of the aircraft types appearing in previous editions and now reappearing in the 1961 edition have undergone some change or modification revealed by the text, photographs or drawings. In conclusion, I should like to record my thanks to John W. R. Taylor, the editor of *Jane's All the World's Aircraft*, and to John Fricker and F. G. Swanborough of *The Aeroplane and Astronautics* for their valuable assistance in obtaining some of the photographs appearing in this edition. WILLIAM GREEN

ACKNOWLEDGEMENTS

THE sources of some of the photographs appearing in this edition are as follows: Charles E. Brown, 136; Gianni Berengo-Gardin, 34, 150, 202, 256; Butler-Green Aviation Photos, 20, 32, 36, 86, 108, 120, 140, 144, 146, 152, 238, 240; G. Cozzika, 16; Crown Copyright, 104; J. B. Cynk, 200; Pierre Jeandrain, 26; N. Matsumura, 46; David W. Menard, 56; J. S. Orwovski, 216; Revista Nacional de Aeronautica, 112; Sahani Bros., 148; Michel Tiziou, 230, 274.
6

N.A.T.O. NAMES FOR SOVIET AIRCRAFT

A SYSTEM of identification names for aircraft of both the Soviet armed forces and civil organisations is employed by the forces of the North Atlantic Treaty Organisation. The system employs a simple key; The names allocated to fighters and fighter-bombers commence with the letter " F ", those for bombers and attack aircraft with the letter " B ", cargo and troop-carrying aircraft have been allocated names commencing with the letter " C ", and the names for miscellaneous aircraft types (e.g. trainers, flying boats, transport gliders) commence with the letter " M ". All rotor-craft have identification names commencing with " H ". Airscrew-driven (both piston-engined and turboprop-powered) machines have identification names possessing only one syllable, and turbojet-driven machines have names containing two syllables. Suffix letters attached to the identification name (e.g. Farmer-B, Farmer-C) indicate a variant of the basic type.

JET FIGHTERS

Faceplate: The MiG-21 single-seat interceptor fighter described and illustrated in the 1960 edition.

Fagot: The MiG-15 single-seat fighter and close-support aircraft illustrated and described in the 1953–6 editions.

Fantail: The Lavochkin La-15 single-seat fighter powered by a 3,500 lb.s.t. RD-500 turbojet and built in relatively small quantities. Illustrated in the 1953 edition. Now obsolete.

Farmer: The MiG-19 single-seat interceptor fighter and close-support aircraft illustrated and described on pages 182–3. Variants include the Farmer-A, -B and -C.

Fishbed-A and -B: A delta-wing interceptor fighter designed by the P.O. Sukhoi bureau and described and illustrated in the 1959 edition.

Fishpot: An all-weather variant of the *Fishbed* described and illustrated in the 1959 edition. The service status of both *Fishpot* and *Fishbed* is uncertain.

Flashlight: The Yak-25 two-seat all-weather and night interceptor fighter described and illustrated in the 1960 edition. The *Flashlight-B* and *Flashlight-C* are respectively light bomber and all-weather fighter developments embodying aerodynamic refinements and afterburning turbojets.

Flora: The Yak-23 single-seat interceptor fighter powered by a 3,500 lb.s.t. RD-500 turbojet and now obsolete. The Yak-23 was illustrated in the 1956 edition.

Fresco: The MiG-17 single-seat day (*Fresco-A, -B and -C*) fighter and (*Fresco-D and -E*) limited all-weather fighter illustrated and described on pages 180–81.

JET BOMBERS

Backfin: A supersonic medium bomber of uncertain design origin which first appeared in 1957.

Badger: The Tupolev Tu-16 medium bomber illustrated and described in the 1960 edition.

Beagle: The Ilyushin Il-28 twin-jet light bomber described and illustrated in the 1959 edition.

Bison: A Myasishchev long-range heavy bomber described and illustrated in the 1960 edition.

Blowlamp: A supersonic light attack bomber illustrated and described in the 1959 edition. Of uncertain design origin, this bomber is not thought to have entered quantity production.

Bosun: The Tupolev Tu-14 twin-jet shore-based naval attack bomber described and illustrated in the 1958 edition.

Bounder: A supersonic delta-wing medium bomber of uncertain design origin reportedly in squadron service and powered by four large, podded turbojets.

Brawny: A twin-jet two-seat attack and close-support monoplane of unknown design origin which first appeared in 1956 and is not believed to have been placed in production.

AIRSCREW-DRIVEN BOMBERS

Bear: The Tupolev Tu-20 long-range heavy bomber described and illustrated in the 1960 edition.

Boot: A turboprop-driven anti-submarine attack aircraft which, powered by a 4,000 s.h.p. Kuznetsov turboprop, appeared in 1956 but does not appear to have been adopted.

Bull: The Tupolev Tu-4, a copy of the Boeing B-29 Superfortress which has now been largely relegated to the transport role.

TRANSPORT AND LIAISON AIRCRAFT

Camel: The Tupolev Tu-104 commercial transport described and illustrated on pages 238-9.

Camp: The Antonov An-8 twin-turboprop assault transport described and illustrated in the 1957 edition.

Cat: The Antonov An-10A and An-12 civil and military transport described and illustrated on pages 16-17. The military version is known to have been under test in 1959.

Cleat: The Tupolev Tu-114 Rossiya long-range commercial transport described and illustrated on pages 240-1.

Clod: The Antonov An-14 light twin-engined S.T.O.L. transport described and illustrated in the 1960 edition.

Coach: The Ilyushin Il-12 civil and military transport described and illustrated in the 1955 edition. Most Il-12's have now been replaced by the Il-14.

Colt: The Antonov An-2 utility biplane described and illustrated in the 1959 edition.

Cooker: The Tupolev Tu-110 four-jet transport evolved from the Tu-104 and described in the 1959 edition. The Tu-110 has now been abandoned in view of the success of the Tu-104B.

Coot: The Ilyushin Il-18 commercial transport described and illustrated on pages 146-7.

Crate: The Ilyushin Il-14 civil and military transport evolved from the Il-12 and described and illustrated in the 1959 edition.

Creek: The Yak-12M civil and military three/four-seat light monoplane illustrated and described in the 1957 edition. The Yak-12R and Yak-12M are dubbed *Creek-A* and *-B* respectively, and the extensively modified Yak-12A is the *Creek-C*.

HELICOPTERS

Hare: The Mil Mi-1 three-seat utility helicopter illustrated and described on page 267.

8

Hen: The Kamov Ka-15 two-seat utility helicopter illustrated and described in the 1958 edition.

Hog: The Kamov Ka-18 four-seat utility helicopter described and illustrated in the 1960 edition.

Hook: The Mil Mi-6 heavy transport helicopter described and illustrated on page 268.

Horse: The Yak-24 heavy transport helicopter described and illustrated on page 283.

Hound: The Mil Mi-4 general-purpose helicopter described and illustrated in the 1960 edition.

MISCELLANEOUS

Madge: The Beriev Be-6 maritime reconnaissance flying boat described and illustrated in the 1958 edition. Now largely relegated to the transport role.

Mare: A Tsibin-designed heavy transport glider now obsolete.

Mascot: The Il-28U training variant of the Il-28 twin-jet light attack bomber described and illustrated in the 1958 edition.

Max: The Yak-18 primary trainer produced in several versions, including the single-seat Yak-18P and two-seat Yak-18A with the Ivchenko AI-14R engine.

Midget: The MiG-15UTI tandem two-seat advanced trainer version of the MiG-15 described and illustrated in the 1958 edition.

Mole: The Yak-14 heavy transport glider now largely replaced by Yak-24 helicopters in Soviet airborne formations.

Moose: The Yak-11 basic trainer described and illustrated in the 1957 edition.

A NOTE ON SOVIET DESIGNATIONS

Some confusion has arisen from the fact that individual aircraft design bureaux in Russia apply their own designations to aircraft which are also designated by the Soviet Air Forces. Normally, when an aircraft is accepted for production for the Soviet Air Forces it is allocated a type number following that of the last aircraft type to be accepted from the design bureau concerned, odd numbers usually being applied to fighters (e.g. MiG-17, MiG-19, MiG-21) and even numbers to other types (e.g. Tu-12, Tu-14, Tu-16). For instance, the first postwar design by Oleg K. Antonov to be accepted for quantity production for the Soviet Air Forces was designated An-2, meteorological research and float-plane versions being officially designated An-2ZA and An-2V respectively. However, the design bureau designations for these variants are An-4 and An-6. The two systems of designating aircraft account for the disparity between the type numbers of such machines as the *Badger* (Tu-16) and its commercial derivative, the *Camel* (Tu-104), the former being the official designation and the latter being the design bureau designation. A further example of this is the *Bear* which has the official designation Tu-20 and the design bureau designation Tu-95. A further complication is added by the current Soviet practice of bestowing designations on record-breaking aircraft which are presumably intended to cloak their true identity. For instance, the machine believed to be a Sukhoi delta fighter which attained the world speed record by averaging 1,493 m.p.h. on October 31, 1959, has been referred to as the " E-66."

INTERNATIONAL CIVIL AIRCRAFT
MARKINGS

AN	Nicaragua	HZ	Saudi Arabia
AP	Pakistan	I	Italy
B	Formosa	JA	Japan
CB,CP	Bolivia	JY	Jordan
CC	Chile	JZ	Dutch New
CCCP	Soviet Union		Guinea
CF	Canada	LN	Norway
CN	Morocco	LQ,LV	Argentina
CR-A	Mozambique	LX	Luxembourg
CR-G	Portuguese	LZ	Bulgaria
	Guinea	N	U.S.A.
CR-I	Portuguese India	OB	Peru
CR-L	Angola	OD	Lebanon
CS	Portugal	OE	Austria
CU	Cuba	OH	Finland
CX	Uruguay	OK	Czechoslovakia
D	West Germany	OO	Belgium
DM	East Germany	OY	Denmark
EC	Spain	PH	Netherlands
EI,EJ	Eire	PI-C	Philippines
EL	Liberia	PJ	Dutch W. Indies
EP	Iran	PK	Indonesia
ET	Ethiopia	PP,PT	Brazil
F	France	PZ	Surinam
F-KH	Cambodia	SE	Sweden
F-LA	Laos	SL	Saar
F-O	French Colonies	SN	Sudan
F-OG	Guadeloupe	SP	Poland
G	United Kingdom	SU	United Arab
HA	Hungary		Republic (Egypt)
HB	Switzerland	SX	Greece
HC	Ecuador	TC	Turkey
HH	Haiti	TF	Iceland
HI	Dominica	TG	Guatemala
HK	Colombia	TI	Costa Rica
HL	South Korea	TS	Tunisia
HP	Panama	VH	Australia
HS	Thailand	VP-B	Bahamas

VP-F	Falkland Islands	VR-S	Singapore
VP-G	British Guiana	VR-T	Tanganyika
VP-H	British Honduras	VR-U	Brunei
VP-J	Jamaica	VR-W	Sarawak
VP-K	Kenya	VT	India
VP-L	Leeward Islands	XA,XB,XC	
VP-M	Malta		Mexico
VP-P	West Pacific Isles	XH	Honduras
VP-S	Somaliland	XT	China
VP-T	Trinidad,	XV	Viet Nam
	Tobago	XY	Burma
VP-U	Uganda	YA	Afghanistan
VP-V	Saint Vincent	YE	Yemen
VP-X	Gambia	YI	Iraq
VP-Y	Central African	YJ	New Hebrides
	Federation	YK	United Arab
VP-Z	Zanzibar		Republic (Syria)
VQ-B	Barbados Islands	YR	Rumania
VQ-C	Cyprus	YS	El Salvador
VQ-F	Fiji Islands	YU	Yugoslavia
VQ-G	Grenada	YV	Venezuela
VQ-H	Saint Helena	ZA	Albania
VQ-L	Saint Lucia	ZK,ZL,ZM	
VQ-M	Mauritius		New Zealand
VQ-S	Seychelle Islands	ZP	Paraguay
VQ-Z	Basutoland,	ZS,ZT,ZU	
	Bechuanaland		South Africa
	and Swaziland	3A	Monaco
VR-A	Aden	3X	Guinea
VR-B	Bermuda	4R	Ceylon
VR-H	Hong Kong	4X	Israel
VR-L	Sierra Leone	5A	Libya
VR-N	Nigeria & British	9G	Ghana
	Cameroons	9K	Kuwait
VR-O	Borneo	9M	Malaya
VR-R	Malaya	9T	Congo

The nationality letters and numeral-letter combinations listed above are normally followed by a hyphen and three or four letters, or by a number, or by a combination of letters and numbers. (In some cases above the first registration letter is listed.)

11

AERO BOERO 95

Country of Origin: Argentina.

Type: Three-seat Light Cabin Monoplane.

Power Plant: One Continental C-90-12F four-cylinder horizontally-opposed engine rated at 95 h.p.

Performance: Maximum speed, 127 m.p.h.; cruising speed, 106 m.p.h.; range, 596 mls. at 99 m.p.h.; endurance, 6 hr.

Weights: Empty, 882 lb.; loaded, 1,543 lb.

Development: One of the most recent light aircraft of indigenous design to enter production in Argentina is the Boero 95 produced by the Aero Talleres Boero of Morteros in the province of Córdoba. Of all-metal construction with fabric covering, the Boero 95 is capable of aerobatics, being stressed to 6·6 g., and is intended primarily for flying club and school use, but it may be adapted for the roles of agricultural aircraft and glider tug. It will take-off within 80 yards and land within 55 yards. The prototype Boero 95 flew in 1959, and it is anticipated that the first production deliveries of this aircraft would commence before the end of 1961.

12

AERO BOERO 95

Dimensions: Span, 34 ft. 2 in.; length, 22 ft. 7¾ in.; height, 7 ft. 2 in.

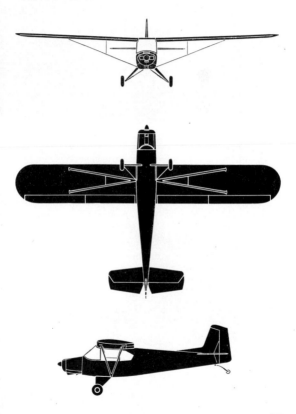

AERO COMMANDER 500B

Country of Origin: U.S.A.

Type: Six/seven-seat Light Transport.

Power Plants: Two Lycoming 10-540 six-cylinder horizontally-opposed engines each rated at 290 h.p.

Performance: Maximum speed, 228 m.p.h. at sea level; cruising speed (70% power), 218 m.p.h. at 10,000 ft.; range (55% power and 30 min. reserve), 1,250 mls.; initial climb, 1,450 ft./min.; service ceiling, 20,500 ft.

Weights: Empty, 4,300 lb.; maximum loaded, 6,750 lb.

Development: The Commander has been in continuous production since 1951, the first production aeroplane, known as the Commander 520, being completed on August 25th of that year. One hundred and fifty Commander 520s were manufactured, and in 1954 this model was superseded by the Model 560 with increased gross weight, eighty of these being built before, in 1955, the Model 560A with a lengthened cabin appeared. Several further models were evolved, including the models 680 and 680E, 560E and 720, and in March 1960 four new models were announced, the Model 500A (260 h.p. Continental 10-470-Ms), the Model 500B (above), the Model 560F (350 h.p. Lycoming IGO 540s), and the Model 680F (360 h.p. Lycoming IGSO-540s). More than 900 Commanders had been delivered by the end of 1960.

14

AERO COMMANDER 500B

Dimensions: Span, 49 ft. 6 in.; length, 35 ft. 1½ in.; height, 14 ft. 6 in.; wing area, 255 sq. ft.

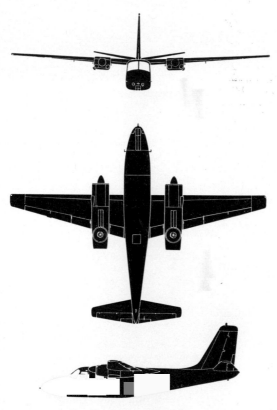

ANTONOV AN-10A UKRAINA (CAT)

Country of Origin: U.S.S.R.

Type: Medium-range Commercial Transport (101 Passengers).

Power Plants: Four Ivchenko AI-20 single-shaft turbo-props each rated at 4,000 e.h.p.

Performance: Maximum continuous cruising speed, 395 m.p.h. at 26,000 ft.; recommended cruising, 370 m.p.h.: normal cruising altitudes, 19,700–32,800 ft.; range (with 32,000-lb. payload), 1,240 mls., (with 18,600-lb. payload), 2,127 mls., (with 23,000-lb. payload), 1,927 mls.; initial climb rate, 1,960 ft./min.

Weights: Normal loaded, 110,200 lb.; maximum loaded, 121,500 lb.

Development: Derived from the unsuccessful 84-passenger An-10, the An-10A entered service with Aeroflot in the autumn of 1959. The An-10 was originally flown with Kuznetsov NK-4 turboprops but the AI-20 was subsequently adopted as standard. A military freighter variant, the An-12 (illustrated by the photograph above) appeared in 1960. The An-12 has a redesigned rear fuselage embodying an integral loading ramp, and revised tail surfaces. A tail gun position is provided. A developed version providing accommodation for 130 passengers in a lengthened fuselage and designated An-16 is believed to be under test.

16

ANTONOV AN-10A UKRAINA (CAT)

Dimensions: Span, 124 ft. 8½ in.; length, 121 ft. 3½ in.;
height, 32 ft. 1¼ in.; wing area, 1,293 sq. ft.

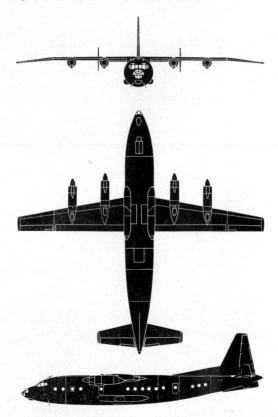

ANTONOV AN-24

Country of Origin: U.S.S.R.

Type: Commercial Transport (32–40 Passengers).

Power Plants: Two Ivchenko turboprops each rated at 2,000 s.h.p.

Performance: Cruising speed, 325 m.p.h. at 20,000 ft.; maximum range, 1,120 mls.; normal stage lengths, 500–750 mls.

Weights: No details available.

Development: Flown for the first time early in 1960, the An-24 is intended to replace the piston-engined Ilyushin Il-14 and will, according to Aeroflot, reduce ton-mile costs by 25%. Although a conventional high wing monoplane, the An-24 is said to employ new lightweight construction methods which reduce structural weight and, in consequence, increase payload. In roughly the same category as the Avro 748, Handley Page Herald and Fokker Friendship, the An-24 features similar anhedral outer wing panels to those of the earlier An-10 and An-12 transports. An interesting feature of the design is the manner in which the tips of the engine nacelles move with the long-span flaps. All undercarriage members are twin-wheel units, and the An-24 is intended to operate from relatively small airfields.

18

ANTONOV AN-24

Dimensions: No details available for publication.

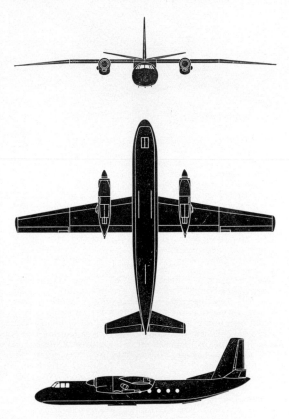

ARMSTRONG WHITWORTH ARGOSY C.1

Country of Origin: Great Britain.
Type: Military Tactical Transport.
Power Plants: Four Rolls-Royce Dart R.Da.8 single-shaft turboprops each rated at 2,500 e.h.p.
Performance: Average cruising speed (80,000 lb.), 268 m.p.h. at 20,000 ft.; range (20% reserves), 576 mls. with 29,000 lb. payload, 1,382 mls. with 20,000 lb. payload; maximum range (with auxiliary fuel tanks), 3,455 mls.; ceiling (90,000 lb.), 21,000 ft.
Weights: Basic weight, 56,000 lb.; maximum loaded, 97,000 lb.; maximum payload, 29,000 lb.
Development: A military version of the commercial Argosy 650 freighter, the first pre-production example of which flew on January 8, 1959, the A.W.660 Argosy C.1 is in production for the R.A.F., fifty-six having been ordered. The development prototype for the Argosy C.1 with " crocodile jaw " rear loading doors which can be opened in flight flew on July 28, 1960, and the first production Argosy C.1 was completed in December 1960. The Argosy C.1 can carry sixty-nine troops, forty-eight stretcher cases, two light anti-aircraft guns, or alternative loads. The commercial Argosy 650 has 2,100 e.h.p. Dart R.Da.7s, and among future operators are Riddle Airlines.

ARMSTRONG WHITWORTH ARGOSY C.1

Dimensions: Span, 115 ft.; length, 88 ft. 1 in.; height, 27 ft.; wing area, 1,458 sq. ft.

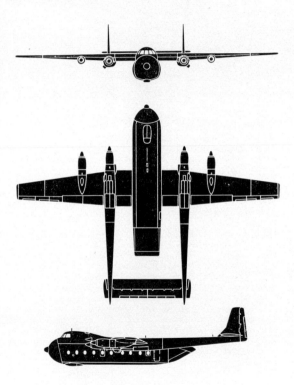

AUSTER D.6/180

Country of Origin: Great Britain.
Type: Four-seat Light Cabin Monoplane.
Power Plant: One Lycoming O-360 four-cylinder horizontally-opposed engine rated at 180 h.p.
Performance: (At 2,400 lb.) Maximum speed, 138 m.p.h. at sea level; maximum cruising speed, 133 m.p.h. at 5,000 ft.; range at maximum cruising speed, 490 mls.; initial climb rate, 850 ft./min.
Weights: Empty, 1,450 lb.; maximum loaded, 2,500 lb.
Development: The Auster "D" series of light aircraft appeared in the Spring of 1960. This series includes the two-seat D.4/108 powered by a 108 h.p. Lycoming 0/235; the three-seat D.5/160 with a 160 h.p. Lycoming O-230, and the four-seat D.6/180 described and illustrated here. The standard Auster welded steel-tube, fabric-covered fuselage structure is employed, but metal wing spars replace the wooden spars employed by earlier Auster types. The "D" models can be supplied with 32 ft. or 36 ft. wings. The short-span wings will result in increased level speeds and reduced climb rates. The first production D.4/108 flew on February 12, 1960, and a large number of D.4s and D.5s are being produced for the Portuguese Government. The D.6/180 flew for the first time on May 9, 1960. The projected D.8 is reported to be basically a D.6 with a nosewheel undercarriage.

AUSTER D.6/180

Dimensions: Span, 36 ft.; length, 23 ft. 2 in.; height, (over airscrew) 8 ft. 1 in.; wing area, 184·5 sq. ft.

AVIAMILANO P.19 SCRICCIOLO

Country of Origin: Italy.

Type: Two-seat Light Training Monoplane.

Power Plant: One Continental C90-12F four-cylinder horizontally-opposed engine rated at 95 h.p.

Performance: Maximum speed, 125 m.p.h.; cruising speed, 109 m.p.h.; initial climb rate, 700 ft./min.; service ceiling, 17,060 ft.; normal range, 410 mls.

Weights: Empty, 882 lb.; loaded, 1,389 lb.

Development: The P.19 Scricciolo has been designed in competition with the Partenavia P.59 Jolly to meet Italian Aero Club requirements for a standard club training and touring aircraft. The prototype was flown for the first time in the summer of 1960, and an initial series of twenty-five aircraft are under construction. The Scricciolo can be fitted with any " flat-four " engine of 80–100 h.p., and a proposed alternative to the Continental engine is the 83 h.p. Agusta GA.70/0. Side-by-side seating is provided and the structure comprises a welded steel-tube fuselage, a wooden single-spar wing and metal control surfaces. An all-metal stressed-skin wing is under consideration, and proposed developments include a version with a fixed nosewheel undercarriage. A glider tug variant with a fixed tailwheel undercarriage and a 140 h.p. engine is projected.

AVIAMILANO P.19 SCRICCIOLO

Dimensions: Span, 33 ft. 7 in.; length, 22 ft. 11 in.;
height, 6 ft. 9 in.; wing area, 150·7 sq. ft.

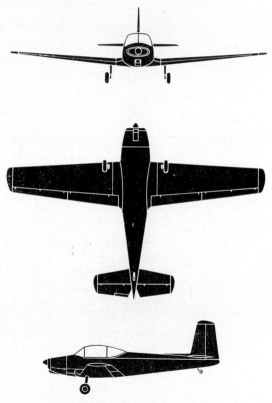

AVRO CF-100 MK. 5

Country of Origin: Canada.

Type: Two-seat All-weather Interceptor Fighter.

Power Plants: Two Orenda Engines, Orenda 11 single-shaft turbojets each rated at 7,275 lb.s.t.

Performance: Maximum speed, 650 m.p.h. at 10,000 ft.; 587 m.p.h. at 40,000 ft. (Mach 0·89); initial climb rate, 8,500 ft./min.; service ceiling, 54,000 ft.; combat radius on internal fuel, 650 mls.; range with maximum external fuel, 2,000 (plus) mls.

Weights: Empty, 23,100 lb.; normal loaded, 33,600 lb.; maximum, 36,000 lb.

Armament: Fifty-two 2·75-in. spin-stabilised unguided rockets in each of two wingtip pods.

Development: The CF-100 Mk. 5 was the last production variant of this Canadian all-weather fighter, 692 examples of which had been produced when production terminated in December 1958. Of these, fifty-three Mk. 5s were supplied to the Belgian Air Force. The replacement of CF-100 Mk. 5s with home-based R.C.A.F. units by McDonnell F-101B Voodoo fighters is expected to commence in 1961. At one time it was proposed to manufacture the CF-100 Mk. 6 with Orenda 11R turbojets equipped with Bristol simplified reheat and a Marquardt two-position nozzle and offering 8,250 lb.s.t. This variant was to have carried Sparrow II missiles.

AVRO CF-100 MK. 5

Dimensions: Span (over missile pods), 60 ft. 10 in.; length, 54 ft. 2 in.; height, 14 ft. 6 in.; wing area, 591 sq. ft.

AVRO 748 SERIES 1

Country of Origin: Great Britain.
Type: Short- and Medium-haul Commercial Transport (40–44 Passengers).
Power Plants: Two Rolls-Royce Dart 514 (R.Da.6) single-shaft turboprops each rated at 1,740 e.h.p.
Performance: Maximum recommended cruising speed, 265 m.p.h. at 20,000 ft.; range (maximum payload: 9,666 lb.), 668 mls., (maximum fuel), 1,800 mls.
Weights: Basic, 19,444 lb.; max. loaded, 33,000 lb.
Development: Flown for the first time on June 24, 1960, the Avro 748 will enter service in the summer of 1961 with Skyways and B.K.S., these companies having ordered three and five Series 1 aircraft respectively. The Series 2 version, three of which have been ordered by Aden Airways for delivery in 1962, differs in having Dart 531 (R.Da.7) engines rated at 2,105 e.h.p. and the higher take-off weight of 36,000 lb. The Avro 748 has been adopted by the Indian Air Force and is to be built at Kanpur, this factory initially assembling Series 1 aircraft from British-manufactured components and subsequently building a military version of the Series 2 designated Type 757. The first Kanpur-assembled machine is scheduled to fly in the spring of 1961. Two prototypes of the Series 1 have been built, and the prototype Series 2 is scheduled to fly in mid-1961. Production of an initial batch of sixty Avro 748s is in hand.

AVRO 748 SERIES 1

Dimensions: Span, 95 ft.; length, 67 ft.; height, 24 ft. 10 in.; wing area, 795 sq. ft.

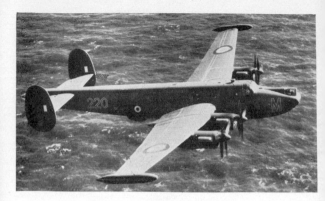

AVRO SHACKLETON M.R.3

Country of Origin: Great Britain.

Type: Long-range Maritime Reconnaissance Bomber.

Power Plants: Four Rolls-Royce Griffon 57A twelve-cylinder liquid-cooled inline engines each rated at 2,450 h.p.

Performance: Maximum speed, 260 m.p.h. at 12,000 ft.; maximum cruising speed, 253 m.p.h.; patrol endurance, (radome extended) 9 hr.; initial climb rate, 850 ft./min.; service ceiling, 19,200 ft.; range (at 200 m.p.h. at 1,500 ft.), 3,662 mls.; normal radius of action, 1,150 mls.

Weights: Empty, 57,800 lb.; max. loaded, 100,000 lb.

Armament: Two 20-mm. cannon in nose and various combinations of bombs, depth charges and mines.

Development: The Shackleton M.R.3 first flew on September 2, 1955, and differs from the earlier M.R.2 in having a nosewheel undercarriage, wingtip tanks, and other changes. A number of the initial model, the M.R.1, have been converted as T.4 navigation trainers.

AVRO SHACKLETON M.R.3

Dimensions: Span, 119 ft. 10 in.; length, 92 ft. 6 in.;
height, 23 ft. 4 in.; wing area, 1,421 sq. ft.

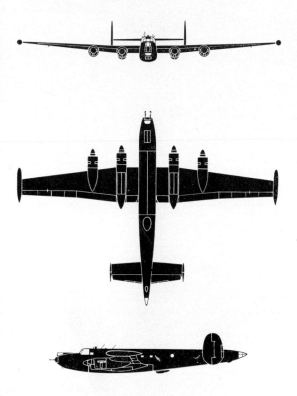

AVRO VULCAN B.2

Country of Origin: Great Britain.
Type: Long-range Medium Bomber.
Power Plants: Four Bristol Siddeley Olympus 201 two-spool turbojets each rated at 17,000 lb.s.t.
Estimated Performance: Maximum speed, 620 m.p.h. at 40,000 ft. (Mach 0·94); typical endurance, 8 hrs.; unrefuelled range, 3,000–4,000 mls.; service ceiling, 60,000 ft.
Weights: Approximate maximum loaded, 200,000 lb.
Armament: One Avro Blue Steel Mk.1 rocket-propelled, guided, supersonic-cruise air-to-surface missile or various combinations of nuclear or conventional free-falling weapons.
Development: The current version of the Vulcan for R.A.F. Bomber Command, the B.2 differs from the Vulcan B.1 in having a 12 ft. greater wing span and Olympus 201s in place of the 13,000 lb.s.t. Olympus 104s. The first production Vulcan B.2 flew in August 1958, the first squadron delivery being made on July 1, 1960, and bombers of this type will replace the Vulcan B.1s in squadron service, the earlier aircraft being used to equip three new squadrons. Unofficial reports have mentioned a " Phase Six " Vulcan with more powerful Olympus turbojets, a modified wing and provision for the carriage of two or more Douglas Skybolt air-launched ballistic missiles. The swollen tail of the Vulcan B.2 performs aerodynamic area-rule functions as well as housing electronic equipment and an enlarged rearward-looking radar.

32

AVRO VULCAN B.2

Dimensions: Span, 111 ft.; length, 99 ft. 11 in.; height,
27 ft. 2 in.; wing area, 3,964 sq. ft.

BEECH MODEL 33 DEBONAIR

Country of Origin: U.S.A.

Type: Four-seat Light Cabin Monoplane.

Power Plant: One Continental 10-470-J six-cylinder horizontally-opposed engine rated at 225 h.p.

Performance: Maximum speed, 195 m.p.h. at sea level; maximum cruising speed, 185 m.p.h. at 7,000 ft.; initial climb rate, 1,010 ft./min.; service ceiling, 19,800 ft.; range (70% power), 720 mls. at 183 m.p.h., (65% power), 770 mls. at 180 m.p.h., (45% power), 850 mls. at 143 m.p.h.

Weights: Empty, 1,730 lb.; loaded, 2,900 lb.

Development: Flown for the first time on September 14, 1959, the Model 33 Debonair is similar in configuration to the Model 35 Bonanza except for its swept vertical tail surfaces. Lighter than the Bonanza, it has a simplified interior and less elaborate equipment. Of all-metal construction, the Debonair has a semi-monocoque aluminium alloy fuselage, and each wing panel is a two-cell semi-monocoque box-beam. Auxiliary fuel tanks may be installed in the wings to increase maximum range to 1,170 miles. Some three hundred Debonairs were produced during 1960.

34

BEECH MODEL 33 DEBONAIR

Dimensions: Span, 32 ft. 9⅞ in.; length, 25 ft. 6 in.; height, 6 ft. 3 in.; wing area, 177·6 sq. ft.

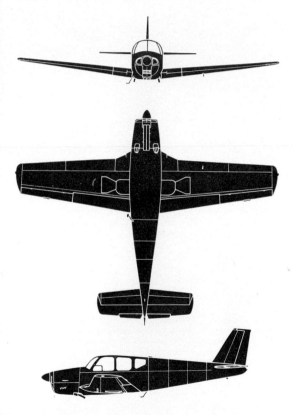

BLACKBURN B.103 BUCCANEER

Country of Origin: Great Britain.

Type: Two-seat Shipboard Low-level Strike Aircraft.

Power Plants: Two de Havilland Gyron Junior 101 (D.G.J. 2) single-shaft turbojets each rated at 7,100 lb.s.t.

Estimated Performance: Maximum speed, 720 m.p.h. at sea level (Mach 0·95); tactical radius, 500–600 mls.

Weights: Approximate loaded, 42,000 lb.

Armament: Tactical nuclear or conventional weapons in internal weapons bay with rotary door.

Development: First flown on April 30, 1958, the Buccaneer is scheduled to enter service with the Royal Navy in 1962, and the last six Buccaneers of a development batch of twenty machines ordered in July 1955 are to be employed for initial service trials by the Handling Squadron during 1961. An order for an additional fifty machines was placed on September 30, 1959. The Buccaneer has blown wings, tailplane leading edges, flaps and drooping ailerons.

36

BLACKBURN B.103 BUCCANEER

Dimensions: Span, 42 ft. 6 in.; length, 62 ft. 4 in.; height, 16 ft.

BLUME BL 502

Country of Origin: Federal German Republic.
Type: Four-seat Light Cabin Monoplane.
Power Plant: One Lycoming O-320-A four-cylinder
horizontally-opposed engine rated at 150 h.p.
Performance: Maximum speed, 155 m.p.h. at sea level;
cruising speed (70% power), 137 m.p.h.; range, 559
mls. at 116 m.p.h.; initial climb rate, 1,005 ft./min.;
ceiling, 15,750 ft.; endurance, 4·1 hr.
Weights: Empty, 1,478 lb.; loaded 2,470 lb.
Development: Designed by Professor Dipl.-Ing. Walter
Blume who, as chief engineer of the Arado Flugzeugwerke G.m.b.H., was responsible for a number of out-
standing designs including the Arado Ar 79 two-seat
cabin monoplane which established a number of International Class Records in 1938, and the Ar 234B Blitz,
the world's first operational jet bomber, the Bl 502
is one of two current developments of the basic Bl 500
design, a prototype of which, built by the Focke-Wulf
G.m.b.H., flew on March 14, 1957. These are the
Bl 502 described above and the Bl 503, the latter
differing in having a 180 h.p. Lycoming O-360-A1A
engine. Fully aerobatic two-seat training versions of
both the Bl 502 and Bl 503 are proposed. The Bl 501
was to have been a version of the basic design powered
by a 125 h.p. engine.

BLUME BL 502

Dimensions: Span, 34 ft. 5⅓ in.; length, 26 ft. 8¾ in.; height, 7 ft. 10½ in.; wing area, 161·459 sq. ft.

BOEING MODEL 707-420

Country of Origin: U.S.A.

Type: Long-range Commercial Transport (Max. Passengers: 189).

Power Plants: Four Rolls-Royce Conway 508 (R.Co.12) by-pass turbojets each rated at 17,500 lb.s.t.

Performance: Maximum cruising speed, 603 m.p.h. at 25,000 ft.; long-range cruising speed, 523 m.p.h. at 40,000 ft.; range (max. fuel), 6,955 mls. at 521 m.p.h. at 39,000 ft., (max. payload), 4,710 mls.

Weights: Empty 124,020 lb.; max. take-off, 312,000 lb.

Development: The designation " Model 707 " covers a family of closely related transports. These are:

Model 707-120: Domestic model powered by 13,000 lb.s.t. (wet) JT3C-6 turbojets ordered by PanAm, American, Continental, T.W.A., Qantas and Cubana. Dimensions: span, 130 ft. 10 in.; length, 144 ft. 6 in.; height, 38 ft. 5 in; wing area, 2,433 sq. ft.

Model 707-220: Domestic model similar to the -120 apart from 15,500 lb.s.t. (dry) JT4A-3 turbojets and reduced length (134 ft. 6 in.) operated by Braniff.

Model 707-320: Intercontinental model with similar power plants to -220 and similar dimensions to -420 ordered by PanAm, Air France, Sabena, T.W.A. etc.

Model 707-420: Described above and illustrated. Ordered by B.O.A.C., Air-India, Lufthansa and Varig.

Retrofitted with 17,000 lb.s.t. JT3D-1 turbofan engines the Model 707-120 becomes the -120B. The last two digits of the suffix of the basic designation are assigned to the specific airline.

BOEING MODEL 707-420

Dimensions: Span, 142 ft. 5 in.; length, 152 ft. 11 in.; height, 38 ft. 8 in.; wing area, 2,892 sq. ft.

BOEING MODEL 720-020

Country of Origin: U.S.A.

Type: Medium-range Commercial Transport (Max. Passengers: 153).

Power Plants: Four Pratt and Whitney JT3C-7 two-spool turbojets each rated at 12,000 lb.s.t. (dry).

Performance: Maximum continuous cruising speed, 600 m.p.h. at 25,000 ft.; long-range cruising speed, 535 m.p.h. at 40,000 ft.; range (max. fuel), 4,260 mls. at 535 m.p.h. at 37,500 ft., (max. payload), 3,178 mls.

Weights: Empty, 99,919 lb.; max. take-off, 202,000 lb.

Development: The Model 720, flown for the first time on November 23, 1959, is the smallest of current Boeing transports and is, from the weight and structural strength viewpoints, a completely new design. Generally similar externally to the earlier Model 707-220, the Model 720 incorporates design refinements, including a leading-edge " glove " which extends the wing chord between the fuselage and inner engine pod. Three " lift-booster " leading-edge flaps are fitted on each side, a slightly smaller and lighter undercarriage, and taller, redesigned tail surfaces are other features. The Model 720B has 17,000 lb.s.t. JT3D-1 turbofans. Purchasers include Lufthansa, American Airlines, Braniff, Avianca, Irish Airlines, United Airlines and Western.

BOEING MODEL 720-020

Dimensions: Span, 130 ft. 10 in.; length, 136 ft. 2 in.;
height, 38 ft. 4 in.; wing area, 2,433 sq. ft.

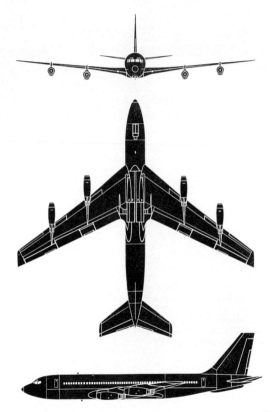

BOEING B-52G STRATOFORTRESS

Country of Origin: U.S.A.

Type: Long-range Heavy Bomber and Missile Carrier.

Power Plants: Eight Pratt and Whitney J57-P-43W turbojets each rated at 13,750 lb.s.t. (wet) and 11,200 lb.s.t. (dry).

Performance: Approximate maximum speed, 665 m.p.h. at 20,000 ft. (Mach 0·95), 614 m.p.h. at 40,000 ft. (Mach 0·93); service ceiling, 55,000 ft.; maximum ceiling, 59,000 ft.; maximum unrefuelled flight range, 9,000 mls.

Weights: Maximum loaded, 488,000 lb.

Armament: Two North American GAM-77 Hound Dog air-to-surface missiles on underwing pylons, and various loads of conventional and thermonuclear free-falling weapons internally. Defensive armament comprises two 20-mm. cannon in remotely-controlled tail barbette.

Development: The last B-52G was completed late in 1960, its place on the production line being taken by the extensively modified B-52H with 17,000 lb.s.t. Pratt and Whitney TF-33-P-3 turbofan engines. Intended primarily as a launching platform for the GAM-87A Sky Bolt ballistic missile, the B-52H has a 490,000 lb. gross weight and a six-barrel rotary cannon in the tail barbette.

BOEING B-52G STRATOFORTRESS

Dimensions: Span, 185 ft.; length, 157 ft. 6⅞ in.; height, 40 ft. 8 in.; wing area, 4,000 sq. ft.

BOEING RB-47H STRATOJET

Country of Origin: U.S.A.
Type: Radar and Photo Reconnaissance Aircraft.
Power Plants: Six General Electric J47-GE-25A single-shaft turbojets each rated at 7,200 lb.s.t (wet).
Performance: Max. speed, 650 m.p.h. at 20,000 ft. (Mach 0·93); max. range (internal fuel), 3,200 mls. at 495 m.p.h. at 38,000 ft. (Mach 0·75); service ceiling, 42,000 ft.
Weights: (B-47E/II) Normal loaded, 175,000 lb.; maximum loaded, 202,000 lb.
Armament: Two 20-mm. cannon in tail position.
Development: The RB-47H is a " special " reconnaissance version of the B-47E medium bomber, employed for oblique radar mapping and reconnaissance, and the monitoring of radio and radar transmissions. The bomb-bay is replaced by a pressurised compartment for three electronic specialists, increasing the crew to a total of six. The last Stratojet was completed in February 1957, and remaining bombers of this type have been brought up to B-47E/II standards with a strengthened wing for low-altitude operations.
46

BOEING RB-47H STRATOJET

Dimensions: Span, 116 ft.; length, 109 ft. 10 in.;
height, 27 ft. 11 in.; wing area, 1,400 sq. ft.

BREGUET 1050 ALIZÉ

Country of Origin: France.
Type: Three-seat Shipboard Anti-submarine Aircraft.
Power Plant: One Rolls-Royce Dart R.Da.21 single-shaft turboprop rated at 2,100 e.s.h.p.
Performance: Maximum speed, 285 m.p.h. at sea level, 292 m.p.h. at 10,000 ft.; initial climb rate, 1,380 ft./min.; service ceiling (at 17,650 lb.), 20,000 ft.; endurance (with standard internal fuel at 144 m.p.h.), 5 hr. 12 min. at 1,500 ft., 5 hr. 10 min. at 15,000 ft.; maximum endurance (with additional 105 Imp. gal. tank in weapons bay), 7 hr. 40 min. at 15,000 ft.; maximum ferry range, 1,555–1,785 mls.
Weights: Empty, 12,566 lb.; normal loaded, 18,100 lb.
Armament: Three 353-lb. depth charges or one torpedo internally and two 353-lb. or 386-lb. depth charges and six 5-in. rockets or two Nord SS.11M air-to-surface missiles underwing.
Development: Orders for the Alizé were nearing completion at the end of 1960, these including seventy-five machines for the French Navy, the first of which flew on March 26, 1959, and approximately a dozen machines for the Indian Navy, the first of which flew in October 1960. The first prototype Alizé (Tradewind) flew on October 6, 1956, this being followed by two further prototypes and two pre-production aircraft.

48

BREGUET 1050 ALIZÉ

Dimensions: Span, 51 ft. 2 in.; length, 45 ft. 6 in.; height, 15 ft. 7 in.; wing area, 387·5 sq. ft.

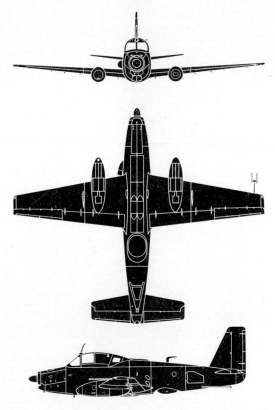

BRISTOL BRITANNIA C.1

Country of Origin: Great Britain.

Type: Long-range Military Freight and Troop-carrying Aircraft (110–115 Passengers).

Power Plants: Four Bristol Siddeley Proteus 255 turbo-props each rated at 4,445 e.h.p.

Performance: Maximum speed (at 150,000 lb.), 401 m.p.h. at 21,000 ft.; maximum range, 5,230 mls.; range (maximum payload—37,417 lb.), 4,170 mls.; initial climb rate (185,000 lb.), 1,300 ft./min.; service ceiling, 30,000 ft.

Weights: Basic operational, 96,826 lb.; maximum loaded, 185,000 lb.

Development: The Britannia C.1, first flown on December 29, 1958, and now serving with Nos. 99 and 511 Squadrons of R.A.F. Transport Command, differs from the final commercial production model, the Britannia 320, principally in having a large freight loading door, and a heavy duty floor. Twenty Britannia C.1s were ordered, and R.A.F. Transport Command also operates three Britannia C.2s which have only the forward floor strengthened for heavy freighting, the main body of the fuselage being intended principally for trooping. The manufacture of more than eighty Britannias of various sub-types was virtually complete at the end of 1960. Only fifteen examples of the initial Britannia 102 were built (for B.O.A.C.), production subsequently concentrating on the larger and more powerful commercial Britannia 300, 310 and 320 models which are externally similar to the Britannia C.1.

BRISTOL BRITANNIA C.1

Dimensions: Span, 142 ft. 3½ in.; length, 124 ft. 3 in.; height, 36 ft. 8⅓ in.; wing area, 2,075 sq. ft.

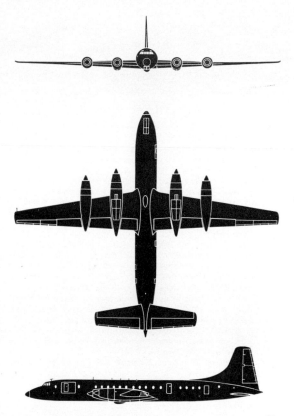

CANADAIR CL-28 ARGUS MK. 2

Country of Origin: Canada.
Type: Long-range Maritime Reconnaissance Aircraft.
Power Plants: Four Wright R-3350 TC981 EA-1 Turbo Compound engines each rated at 3,400 h.p. (dry) and 3,700 h.p. (wet).
Performance: Maximum speed, 288 m.p.h. at sea level; maximum cruising speed, 203 m.p.h. at 5,000 ft.; patrol endurance (at 190 m.p.h. below 1,000 ft. and allowing for 575-ml. diversion on return), 12 hr. at range of 830 mls., 8 hr. at range of 1,210 mls., 4 hr. at range of 1,590 mls.
Weights: Empty, 81,000 lb.; loaded, 148,000 lb.
Armament: Various combinations of mines, nuclear and conventional depth charges, active and passive homing torpedoes, and bombs up to 8,000 lb. in two fuselage bays, and up to 7,600 lb. on pylons.
Development: Employing the wings, tail surfaces, flight controls and undercarriage of the Bristol Britannia, the Argus was flown for the first time on March 28, 1957, and the first thirteen production aircraft were of the Mk. 1 version with American search radar in a larger " chin " housing. The Argus Mk. 2 employs British search radar, and twenty of this version were built for the R.C.A.F., the last being completed on July 13, 1960. Currently serving with Nos. 404 and 405 Squadrons, the Argus had flown a total of some 21,000 hours by July 1, 1960.

CANADAIR CL-28 ARGUS MK. 2

Dimensions: Span, 142 ft. 3½ in.; length, 128 ft. 3 in.; height, 36 ft. 8½ in.; wing area, 2,075 sq. ft.

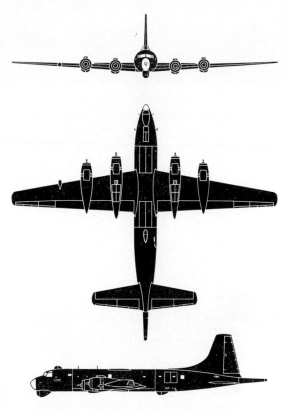

CANADAIR CL-44D-4

Country of Origin: Canada.
Type: Long-range Freight Transport.
Power Plants: Four Rolls-Royce Tyne 515/10 (R. Ty.12) twin-shaft two-spool turboprops each rated at 5,730 e.h.p.
Performance: Recommended maximum cruising speed (165,000 lb.) 391 m.p.h. at 20,000 ft.; economical cruising speed, 368 m.p.h. at 30,000 ft.; range with maximum payload (66,480 lb.), 5,205 mls.; range (with centre section auxiliary fuel tank), 6,448 mls.
Weights: Empty, 86,889 lb.; operating empty weight, 88,520 lb.; maximum loaded, 205,000 lb.
Development: Derived basically from the Bristol Britannia, the CL-44D-4 is the largest commercial freighter in the world and, featuring a hinged tail for rear loading, has been ordered by the Flying Tiger Line (10 aircraft), Seaboard and Western (five aircraft), and Slick Airways (two aircraft). The first CL-44D-4 was rolled out in August 1960, and the freighter will enter service in 1961. A military personnel and freight transport variant, the CL-44-6, is being manufactured for the R.C.A.F. as the CC-106, and the first aircraft of this type flew on November 15,1959. The CL-44-6, twelve of which are being built, does not have the hinged tail, and this type is illustrated by the photograph. Forty CL-44s are expected to be supplied to the U.S.A.F., and the CL-44D-5 and -6 will have Tyne R.Ty.14 engines.

CANADAIR CL-44D-4

Dimensions: Span, 142 ft. 3⅜ in.; length, 136 ft. 10¾ in.; height, 36 ft. 7¾ in.; wing area, 2,075 sq. ft.

CANADAIR CL-13B SABRE MK. 6

Country of Origin: Canada.

Type: Single-seat Day Interceptor Fighter.

Power Plant: One Orenda Engine, Orenda 14 single-shaft turbojet rated at 7,275 lb.s.t.

Performance: Maximum speed, 710 m.p.h. at sea level (Mach 0·933), 680 m.p.h. at 10,000 ft. (Mach 0·925), 620 m.p.h. at 36,000 ft. (Mach 0·94); initial climb rate, 11,800 ft./min.; time to 40,000 ft., 6 min.; tactical radius (on internal fuel), 363 mls.; maximum range (with maximum external fuel), 1,495 mls.

Weights: Empty, 10,811–11,143 lb.; combat weight, 14,044 lb.; maximum loaded, 17,611 lb.

Armament: Six 0·5-in. Colt-Browning machine guns.

Development: The Sabre Mk. 6 was the final Canadian development of the licence-built North American F-86E Sabre, and the last of 390 aircraft of this type to be produced was completed on October 9, 1958. Of these, 225 were supplied to the German Federal Republic, thirty-four were purchased by South Africa and six were purchased by Colombia. The Sabre Mk. 1 was identical to the F-86A and only one example was built. This was followed by 350 Sabre Mk. 2s identical to the F-86E, one Mk. 3 with an Orenda 3, 437 Mk. 4s with cabin air conditioning modifications, and 370 Mk. 5s with the 6,355 lb.s.t. Orenda 10.

CANADAIR CL-13B SABRE MK. 6

Dimensions: Span, 37 ft. 1 in.; length, 37 ft. 6 in.; height, 14 ft. 7 in.; wing area, 304 sq. ft.

CENTRE EST-JODEL DR.1050
AMBASSADEUR

Country of Origin: France.
Type: Three-seat Light Cabin Monoplane.
Power Plant: One Continental O-200A four-cylinder horizontally-opposed engine rated at 100 h.p.
Performance: Maximum speed, 137 m.p.h. at 9,020 ft.; cruising speed, 130 m.p.h. at 8,200 ft.; range, 560 mls. at 128 m.p.h. at 6,560 ft., 683 mls. at 99 m.p.h. at 6,560 ft.; initial climb rate, 630 ft./min.; service ceiling, 16,400 ft.
Weights: Empty, 915 lb.; loaded, 1,653 lb.
Development: A three-seater derived from the popular two-seat Jodel D.11 by Monsieur P. Robin, the DR.1050 is the latest production version of the DR.100 Ambassadeur which is also built by the Société Aéronautique Normande. Whereas the DR.100 has the 90 h.p. Continental C90-14F engine, the DR.105 and DR.1050 have the more powerful Continental O-200A. The DR.1050, which obtained its Certificat de Navigabilité on March 11, 1960, differs from the DR.105 solely in its fuel system, instrumentation, and certain minor details. The DR.1050 Ambassadeur's cabin accommodates two persons side-by-side with dual controls with the third seat located centrally behind, but there is sufficient room to accommodate an additional passenger over short ranges.

CENTRE EST-JODEL DR.1050 AMBASSADEUR

Dimensions: Span, 28 ft. 7⅓ in.; length, 21 ft. 3 in.; height, 5 ft. 9¾ in.; wing area, 146·389 sq. ft.

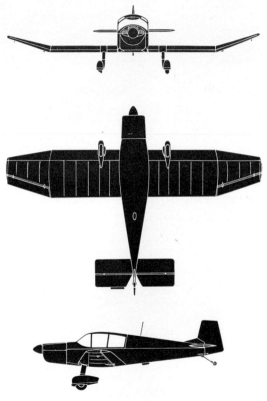

CESSNA 310D

Country of Origin: U.S.A.

Type: Five-seat Cabin Monoplane.

Power Plants: Two Continental IO-470-D six-cylinder horizontally-opposed engines each rated at 260 h.p.

Performance: Maximum speed, 242 m.p.h. at sea level; maximum recommended cruising speed, 220 m.p.h.; maximum range (with 26 Imp. gal. auxiliary tanks), 1,440 mls. at 171 m.p.h. at 10,000 ft., (with normal fuel), 825 mls. at 218 m.p.h. at 8,000 ft.; initial climb rate, 1,800 ft./min.; service ceiling, 21,300 ft.

Weights: Empty, 3,037 lb.; maximum loaded, 4,830 lb.

Development: The Model 310D differs from its immediate predecessor, the Model 310C, in having swept vertical tail surfaces, this innovation being introduced during 1960. The Model 310 flew initially on January 3, 1953, and 160 examples of the Model 310B (240 h.p. Continental O-470-M engines) were produced for the U.S.A.F. under the designation U-3A, deliveries being completed in November 1958. A further thirty-five were ordered by the U.S.A.F. under the designation U-3B, deliveries commencing in December 1960.

60

CESSNA 310D

Dimensions: Span, 35 ft. 9 in.; length, 29 ft. 7 in.; height, 9 ft. 11¼ in.; wing area, 175 sq. ft.

CESSNA T-37B

Country of Origin: U.S.A.

Type: Two-seat Intermediate Trainer.

Power Plants: Two Continental J69-T-25 turbojets each rated at 1,025 lb.s.t.

Performance: Maximum speed, 425 m.p.h. at 20,000 ft.; normal range, 869 mls. at 360 m.p.h. at 35,000 ft.; maximum range, 931 mls. at 333 m.p.h. at 35,000 ft.; initial climb rate, 3,370 ft./min.; service ceiling, 38,700 ft.

Weights: Empty, 4,056 lb.; loaded, 6,574 lb.

Development: Currently the standard U.S.A.F. intermediate trainer, the first T-37B was delivered on November 6, 1959. Previously, Cessna had produced 416 T-37A trainers which differed from the current production model primarily in having the Continental J69-T-9 turbojets of 920 lb.s.t. each. Other changes in the T-37B include additional navigation and communication equipment, and later M5 ejector seats with larger catapults for higher speed ejection from the aircraft. The first of two prototypes, designated XT-37, was flown on October 12, 1954, and the first production T-37As were delivered in September 1955, although training courses were not initiated until the beginning of 1957 owing to the need for wing strengthening and other modifications. All remaining T-37A trainers had been converted to " B " standards by July 1960, and current production orders are scheduled to be completed by mid-1961. The T-37 is equipped for all exercises not involving armament.

CESSNA T-37B

Dimensions: Span, 33 ft. 10 in.; length, 29 ft. 3 in.; height, 9 ft. 2 in.; wing area, 183·9 sq. ft.

CHAMPION MODEL 7JC TRI-CON

Country of Origin: U.S.A.
Type: Two-seat Light Cabin Monoplane.
Power Plant: One Continental C90-12F four-cylinder
horizontally-opposed engine rated at 95 h.p.
Performance: Maximum speed, 138 m.p.h.; cruising
speed (at 1,450 lb.), 108 m.p.h.; range, 500 mls.;
initial climb rate, 900 ft./min.
Weights: Empty, 968 lb.; loaded, 1,450 lb.
Development: Introduced in April 1960 by the Champion Aircraft Corporation, the Model 7JC Tri-Con is
the latest variant of the Model 7 Champion, the manufacturing rights to which were purchased by this company from the Aeronca Manufacturing Corporation in
June 1954. The first variant of this light plane to be
manufactured by the Champion company was the
Model 7EC with a tailwheel undercarriage and known
as the Traveller. In February 1957, the production
of a version with a nosewheel undercarriage, the Model
7FC Tri-Traveller, began, and the Model 7JC Tri-Con
illustrated here differs from the Traveller and Tri-
Traveller in having a reverse tricycle undercarriage.
Other variants of the Champion design are the Sky-
Trac and Challenger with accommodation for up to
three persons and respectively powered by a 140 h.p.
Lycoming O-290-D2B and a 150 h.p. Lycoming
O-320-A. Apart from their undercarriages, all models
are similar in general appearance to the Tri-Con.
64

CHAMPION MODEL 7JC TRI-CON

Dimensions: Span, 33 ft. 5 in.; length, 21 ft. 8 in.;
height, 7 ft. 6 in.; wing area, 170 sq. ft.

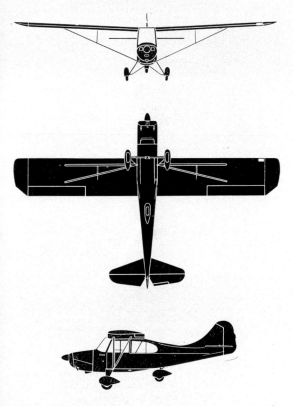

CONVAIR CV-600 MODEL 30

Country of Origin: U.S.A.

Type: Long-range Commercial Transport (96–139 Passengers).

Power Plants: Four General Electric CJ-805-23 aft-fan turbojets each rated at 16,100 lb.s.t.

Performance: Maximum cruising speed, 640 m.p.h. at 21,500 ft.; typical cruising speed (200,000 lb.), 570 m.p.h. at 35,000 ft.; maximum range, 5,527 mls. at 543 m.p.h. at 35,000 ft., range with maximum payload, 4,470 mls.

Weights: Empty, 113,300 lb.; basic operational, 115,275 lb.; maximum loaded, 239,200 lb.

Development: Scheduled to fly for the first time in December 1960, the CV-600 is claimed to fly faster than any other commercial transport. Derived from the CV-880 Model 22, the CV-600 has a longer fuselage and is area-ruled by the addition of " speed capsules " or anti-shock bodies on the wing trailing edges which permit a useful increase in cruising speed. Leading-edge slats and a power-boosted rudder are fitted, these being similar to those adopted for the CV-880 Model 22M. The designation " Model 600 " was adopted by the manufacturers to signify the speed range of the aircraft, and American Airlines propose to redesignate their machines as Model 990s, while those to be operated by S.A.S. and Swissair will be known by the class name of Coronado.

66

CONVAIR CV-600 MODEL 30

Dimensions: Span, 120 ft.; length, 139 ft. 5½ in.; height, 39 ft. 6⅛ in.; wing area, 2,250 sq. ft.

CONVAIR CV-880 MODEL 22

Country of Origin: U.S.A.

Type: Medium-range Commercial Transport (84–110 Passengers).

Power Plants: Four General Electric CJ-805-3 single-shaft turbojets each rated at 11,200 lb.s.t.

Performance: Maximum cruising speed, 615 m.p.h. (Mach 0·89); continuous cruising speed, 557 m.p.h. at 35,000 ft. (Mach 0·84); initial climb rate, 3,700 ft./min.; maximum cruising altitude, 40,000 ft.; range with maximum payload (27,600 lb.), 4,020 mls., with maximum fuel (22,950 lb. payload), 4,350 mls.

Weights: Empty, 81,800 lb.; basic, 89,000 lb.; maximum, 184,500 lb.

Development: The first CV-880 Model 22 was flown on January 27, 1959, and purchasing airlines include Delta, T.W.A., Capital, J.A.L., Transcontinental, R.E.A.L., and C.A.T. of Formosa. Among variants of the basic design are the Model 22M and Model 31. The former is for medium-to-short range routes and differs from the Model 22 in having 11,650 lb.s.t. CJ-805-3B turbojets, leading edge slats, and the power-boosted rudder of the CV-600. The Model 31 is a long-range or international version with a maximum loaded weight of 203,400 lb., a range of 4,260 miles with a capacity payload of 33,600 lb.

68

CONVAIR CV-880 MODEL 22

Dimensions: Span, 120 ft.; length, 129 ft. 4 in.; height, 36 ft. 4 in.; wing area, 2,000 sq. ft.

CONVAIR F-102A DELTA DAGGER

Country of Origin: U.S.A.

Type: Single-seat All-weather Interceptor Fighter.

Power Plant: One Pratt and Whitney J57-P-23 two-spool turbojet rated at 11,700 lb.s.t. (dry) and 17,200 lb.s.t. (afterburning).

Performance: Maximum speed, 825 m.p.h. at 36,000 ft. (Mach 1·25); approximate initial climb rate, 13,000 ft./min.; service ceiling, 54,000 ft.; approximate combat radius (internal fuel), 400 mls.

Weights: Normal loaded, 28,600 lb.; maximum loaded, 32,000 lb.

Armament: Six Hughes GAR-1D radar-guided or GAR-2A infra-red homing Falcon missiles and twenty-four 2·75-in. folding-fin unguided missiles.

Development: Production of the Delta Dagger was terminated in April 1958 after 875 had been delivered to the U.S.A.F. Air Defence Command. Eight squadrons equipped with the Delta Dagger were serving overseas during 1960, in Alaska, Greenland, Germany and Japan, and a gradual reduction of the number of A.D.C. squadrons equipped with the Delta Dagger commenced as the Delta Dart was phased into service. Three Air National Guard squadrons are re-equipping with Delta Daggers, and those remaining on the active U.S.A.F. inventory are being equipped with a time division data link system. Sixty-three examples of a two-seat version, the TF-102A, were procured.

CONVAIR F-102A DELTA DAGGER

Dimensions: Span, 38 ft. 1½ in.; length (including nose probe), 68 ft. 4⅔ in.; height, 21 ft. 2½ in.; wing area, 661·5 sq. ft.

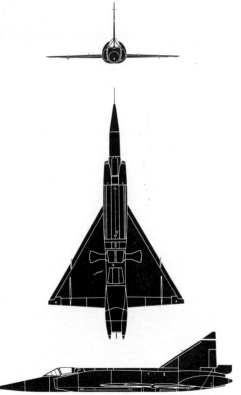

CONVAIR F-106A DELTA DART

Country of Origin: U.S.A.

Type: Single-seat All-weather Interceptor Fighter.

Power Plant: One Pratt and Whitney J75-P-17 two-spool turbojet rated at 17,200 lb.s.t. (dry) and 24,500 lb.s.t. (afterburning).

Performance: Maximum speed, 1,525 m.p.h. at 40,000 ft. (Mach 2·31); maximum manœuvring speed, 1,255 m.p.h. at 40,000 ft. (Mach 1·9); combat radius (internal fuel), 575 mls.; ferry range (maximum external fuel), 2,700 mls. at 610 m.p.h. at 41,000 ft. (Mach 0·92); normal service ceiling, 57,000 ft.; zoom climb altitude, 70,000 ft.

Weights: Approximate empty, 26,000 lb.; normal loaded, 35,000 lb.

Armament: Four Hughes GAR-3 radar-guided or GAR-4 infra-red homing Super Falcon missiles and one Douglas MB-1 Genie missile in internal bay.

Development: The F-106A Delta Dart was flown for the first time on December 26, 1956, and some ten U.S.A.F. Air Defence Command squadrons had either re-equipped with this interceptor or were in process of converting during 1960. The Delta Dart established a new world air speed record of 1,525·95 m.p.h. on December 15, 1959, and the first aircraft of this type equipped with the Hughes MA-1 control system, automatic flight control function and data link, flew early in 1960. Production of a two-seat version, the F-106B, was completed in the Summer of 1960.

CONVAIR F-106A DELTA DART

Dimensions: Span, 38 ft. $1\frac{1}{2}$ in.; length (including nose probe), 70 ft. $8\frac{3}{4}$ in., height, 20 ft. $3\frac{1}{3}$ in.; wing area, $661 \cdot 5$ sq. ft.

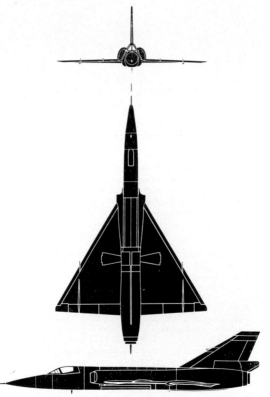

73

CONVAIR B-58A HUSTLER

Country of Origin: U.S.A.
Type: Long-range Medium Bomber.
Power Plants: Four General Electric J79-GE-5B single-shaft variable-stator turbojets each rated at 10,000 lb.s.t. (dry) and 15,600 lb.s.t. (afterburning).
Performance: Maximum speed, 1,385 m.p.h. at 40,000 ft. (Mach 2·1); cruising speed, 595 m.p.h. at 40,000 ft. (Mach 0·9); service ceiling, 60,000 ft.
Est. Weights: Empty, 50,000 lb.; loaded, 160,000 lb.
Armament: A detachable " mission pod " or air-to-surface missile is carried beneath the fuselage, and for defensive purposes a single 20-mm. M.61 Vulcan cannon is installed in a flexible tail cone.
Development: The first U.S.A.F. Hustler unit, the 43rd Bomber Wing, was activated on March 15, 1960, and a second, the 305th, was receiving its equipment at the end of 1960. The first tactically operational B-58A was completed in September 1959, and thirteen of the thirty pre-production and test B-58s have been converted to operational status. Four others have been converted to TB-58 trainers, the first of these (illustrated above) being flown on May 10, 1960. The principal external difference between the TB-58 and the B-58A is the additional cockpit window area of the trainer. Variants projected during 1960 included the B-58C with J58 engines and a range of 6,330 mls. at Mach 2·4; the B-58D long-range interceptor powered by two J58s and carrying six GAR-9 missiles and the similarly powered B-58E tactical bomber.

CONVAIR B-58A HUSTLER

Dimensions: Span, 56 ft. 10 in.; length, 96 ft. 9 in.;
height 31 ft. 5 in.; wing area, 1,542 sq. ft.

DE HAVILLAND COMET 4C

Country of Origin: Great Britain.

Type: Intermediate-range Commercial Transport (72–101 Passengers).

Power Plants: Four Rolls-Royce Avon 525B (RA.29-1) single-shaft turbojets each rated at 10,500 lb.s.t.

Performance: Maximum continuous cruising speed, 500 m.p.h. at 33,000 ft.; typical cruising speed, 472 m.p.h. at 35,000 ft.; range (maximum fuel), 4,285 mls., (maximum payload—22,900 lb.), 3,350 mls.; cruising altitude range, 33,000–39,000 ft.

Weights: Basic operational, 79,600 lb.; maximum take-off, 162,000 lb.

Development: Flown for the first time on October 31, 1959, the Comet 4C has been ordered by Mexicana, Misrair and Middle East Airlines, and five aircraft of this type have been ordered for R.A.F. Transport Command. Third in the Comet 4 series, the Comet 4C combines the wings and fuel tankage of the original Comet 4 with the longer fuselage of the Comet 4B. The first of nineteen Comet 4s for B.O.A.C. flew on April 27, 1958. Six similar aircraft have been supplied to Aerolineas Argentinas, and two have been purchased by the East African Airways Corporation. The Comet 4B was evolved to B.E.A.'s requirements, overall length being increased from 111 ft. 6 in. to 118 ft., wing span being reduced from 115 ft. to 107 ft. 10 in., and the wing-mounted pinion tanks being deleted. This version is operated by both B.E.A. and Olympic Airways. Fifty-six Comet 4s were on order or had been delivered by the end of 1960.

DE HAVILLAND COMET 4C

Dimensions: Span, 114 ft. 10 in.; length, 118 ft.; height, 29 ft. 6 in.; wing area, 2,121 sq. ft.

DE HAVILLAND DOVE 8 (CUSTOM 800)

Country of Origin: Great Britain.
Type: Light Transport and Executive Aircraft (Six Passengers).
Power Plants: Two de Havilland Gipsy Queen 70 Mk.3 six-cylinder inverted engines each rated at 400 h.p.
Performance: Maximum cruising speed, 210 m.p.h.; range cruising speed, 186·5 m.p.h. at 8,000 ft.; initial climb rate, 1,420 ft./min.; maximum range, 1,175 mls.
Weights: Empty 6,580 lb.; loaded, 8,950 lb.
Development: Flown for the first time on February 19, 1960, the Dove 8 is a new and improved model of the well-known light transport which has been in continuous production since 1945. Differing from the previous production model, the Dove 6, in having a Heron-type high-dome canopy, exhaust thrust augmentation tubes and Gipsy Queen 70 Mk. 3 engines in place of the 380 h.p. Gipsy Queen 70 Mk. 2s, the Dove 8 is known in the U.S.A. as the Dove Custom 800. The military personnel transport version of the Dove 4 is known as the Devon C. 1 by the R.A.F. and Sea Devon C. 20 by the Navy. More than 500 Doves had been delivered by the end of 1960.

DE HAVILLAND DOVE 8 (CUSTOM 800)

Dimensions: Span, 57 ft.; length, 39 ft. 6 in.; height, 13 ft. 4 in.; wing area, 335 sq. ft.

DE HAVILLAND DHC-2 BEAVER

Country of Origin: Canada.
Type: Seven-seat Utility Cabin Monoplane.
Power Plant: One Pratt and Whitney R-985 Wasp Junior nine-cylinder air-cooled radial rated at 450 h.p.
Performance: Maximum speed, 163 m.p.h. at 5,000 ft.; cruising speed, 143 m.p.h. at 5,000 ft.; range, 455 mls. at 5,000 ft.; initial climb rate, 1,020 ft./min.; service ceiling, 18,000 ft.
Weights: Empty, 2,850 lb.; loaded, 5,100 lb.
Development: Flown for the first time on August 16, 1947, the Beaver has since been in continuous production and is now serving in both military and civil roles in some fifty countries. On December 17, 1959, it was announced that thirty-six Beavers were to be purchased for the British Army, and deliveries commenced in 1960. The Beaver serves extensively with the U.S.A.F. and the U.S. Army under the respective designations L-20A and L-20, and nearly 1,000 Beavers have been delivered to these services. The Beaver is also employed by the air arms of Australia, Cambodia, Canada, Chile, Colombia, Cuba, Dominica, Finland, France, Iran, Laos, the Netherlands, Peru, South Korea and Uruguay.

DEHAVILLAND DHC-2 BEAVER

Dimensions: Span, 48 ft.; length, 30 ft. 3 in.; height, 9 ft.; wing area, 250 sq. ft.

DE HAVILLAND DHC-3 OTTER

Country of Origin: Canada.

Type: Utility Transport (9–10 Passengers).

Power Plant: One Pratt and Whitney R-1340-S1H1-G or S3H1-G nine-cylinder air-cooled radial rated at 600 h.p.

Performance: Maximum speed, 160 m.p.h. at 5,000 ft.; cruising speed, 138 m.p.h. at 5,000 ft.; maximum range, 960 mls. at 102 m.p.h. at 5,000 ft.; initial climb rate, 735 ft./min.; service ceiling (S1H1-G), 18,800 ft., (S3H1-G), 17,400 ft.

Weights: Empty, 4,168 lb.; loaded, 8,000 lb.

Development: The Otter was flown for the first time on December 12, 1951, and has since been in continuous production. Thirty-nine Otters entered service with the R.C.A.F. in 1953, and a further twenty-seven machines were ordered by this service in 1960. Two hundred and twenty-three Otters had been delivered to the U.S. Army under the designation U-1A by the beginning of 1960; four had been acquired by the U.S. Navy as UC-1s, and the air arms of Chile, Colombia, India and Indonesia have received five, four, twenty-six and seven respectively, while several additional machines are operated by the Royal Norwegian Air Force.

DE HAVILLAND DHC-3 OTTER

Dimensions: Span, 58 ft.; length, 41 ft. 10 in.; height,
12 ft. 7 in.; wing area, 375 sq. ft.

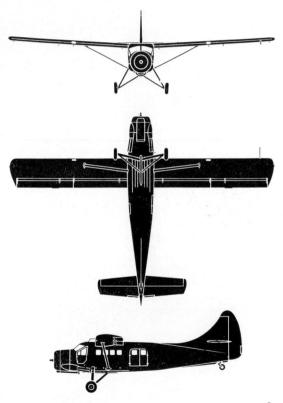

DE HAVILLAND DHC-4 CARIBOU

Country of Origin: Canada.
Type: Utility Transport (30–40 Passengers).
Power Plants: Two Pratt and Whitney R-2000-13 fourteen-cylinder two-row air-cooled radials each rated at 1,450 h.p.
Performance: Maximum speed, 214 m.p.h.; cruising speed (maximum weak mixture), 182 m.p.h. at 7,500 ft., 170 m.p.h. at sea level; en route climb 1,575 ft./min.; service ceiling, 27,700 ft.; range (4,200-lb. payload), 800 mls., (5,685-lb. payload), 400 mls.; max. range, 1,450 mls.
Weights: Empty, 16,850 lb.; max. loaded, 26,000 lb.
Development: The first of two DHC-4 Caribou prototypes flew on July 30, 1958, prior to which date the U.S. Army had placed an order for an evaluation batch of five machines designated YAC-1s. The first of these was delivered to the U.S. Army in October 1959, and the satisfactory results of trials resulted in an order for seven additional machines, deliveries of which began in January 1961, and, subsequently, an order for a further fifteen, deliveries of which are scheduled to commence in May 1961. The AC-1 Caribou can carry twenty-four fully-equipped troops, three tons of freight or fourteen casualty litters. Two Caribous are being evaluated for the Canadian Army as the CC-108, and four are being delivered to the R.C.A.F. for service with U.N.O. forces.

DE HAVILLAND DHC-4 CARIBOU

Dimensions: Span, 96 ft. o½ in.; Length, 72 ft. 7 in.;
height, 31 ft. 9 in.; wing area, 912 sq. ft.

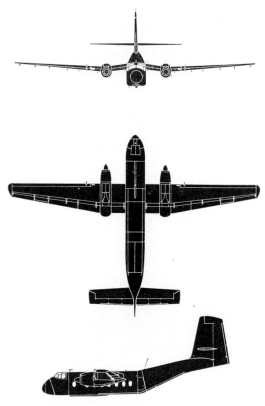

DE HAVILLAND SEA VIXEN F.A.W.1

Country of Origin: Great Britain.
Type: Two-seat Shipboard All-weather Strike Fighter.
Power Plants: Two Rolls-Royce Avon 208 single-shaft turbojets each rated at 10,000 lb.s.t.
Estimated Performance: Maximum speed, 690 m.p.h. at 10,000 ft. (Mach 0·95); initial climb rate, 10,000 ft./min.; time to 40,000 ft., 7–8 min.; service ceiling, 50,000 ft.
Weights: Estimated loaded, 35,000 lb.
Armament: Four de Havilland Firestreak infra-red homing missiles or four Microcell rocket packs each housing twenty-four 2-in. unguided missiles, plus twenty-eight 2-in. missiles in two retractable fuselage packs. (Strike) Twenty-four 3-in. rockets and two 1,000-lb. bombs.
Development: The Sea Vixen was originally ordered in quantity for the Fleet Air Arm in January 1955, and follow-up production contracts were placed in June 1959 and August 1960, present orders being sufficient to maintain production throughout 1961. The first operational squadron to be equipped with the Sea Vixen, No. 892, was commissioned on July 2, 1959, and the Fleet Air Arm will eventually possess a total of six squadrons each with a complement of twelve aircraft.

86

DE HAVILLAND SEA VIXEN F.A.W.1

Dimensions: Span, 50 ft.; length, 55 ft. 7 in.; height, 10 ft. 9 in.; wing area, 648 sq. ft.

DORNIER DO 27H-2

Country of Origin: Federal German Republic.
Type: Six-seat General-purpose S.T.O.L. Monoplane.
Power Plant: One Lycoming GSO-480-B1B6 six-cylinder horizontally-opposed engine rated at 340 h.p.
Performance: Maximum speed, 158 m.p.h. at sea level; 174 m.p.h. at 11,480 ft.; maximum cruising speed, 135 m.p.h. at sea level; cruising speed, 146 m.p.h. at 8,200 ft., 138 m.p.h. at 16,400 ft.; cruising range (max. payload), 492 mls. at 16,400 ft.; service ceiling, 24,600 ft.
Weights: Empty, 2,596 lb.; loaded, 4,070 lb.
Development: The Do 27H-2 which was first flown in November 1958 is the most powerful of the several civil and military variants of the basic design. Four hundred and twenty-eight Do 27A and Do 27B monoplanes, the latter having dual controls, were ordered for the Luftwaffe and the Wehrmacht, and the bulk of these had been delivered by the end of 1960. A six-seat civil version with a 270 h.p. Lycoming GO-480-B1A6 engine is designated Do 27Q-1, and the Do 27Q-4 is similar apart from the provision of an auxiliary fuel tank. The Do 27Q-3 is a four-seat civil model with a 230 h.p. Continental O-470-K engine, and the Do 27S is a twin-float seaplane variant. Fifty Do 27s are being manufactured under licence in Spain.

DORNIER DO 27H-2

Dimensions: Span, 39 ft. 4½ in.; length, 32 ft. 5½ in.; height, 8 ft. 10¾ in.; wing area, 208·82 sq. ft.

DORNIER DO 28

Country of Origin: Federal German Republic.
Type: Six-seat S.T.O.L. General-purpose Light Transport.
Power Plants: Two Lycoming O-540-A1A six-cylinder horizontally-opposed engines each rated at 255 h.p.
Performance: Maximum speed, 171 m.p.h. at sea level; cruising speed (75% power), 162 m.p.h. at 6,000 ft., (60% power), 152 m.p.h.; climb (at 5,130 lb.) to 3,000 ft., 2·4 min., to 6,000 ft., 5 min.; service ceiling (4,970 lb.), 20,500 ft.; range (75% power), 745 mls., (60% power), 660 mls.; endurance (45% power), 5·45 hr.
Weights: Empty, 3,610 lb.; maximum loaded, 5,130 lb.
Development: Derived from the single-engined Do 27, the Do 28 was flown for the first time on April 29, 1959, and has since been the subject of considerable development. Originally powered by two Lycoming O-360-A1A engines each rated at 170 h.p. and possessing a similar wing to that of the Do 27, the second prototype is now powered by Lycoming O-540-A1A engines, and an additional section has been inserted in the wing to increase over-all span. Flown for the first time on March 20, 1960, the second prototype is representative of the production model, and initial customers for the Do 28 include the Deutsche Taxiflug G.m.b.H. and Protea Airways, the latter concern planning to use five aircraft of this type on feeder services in South Africa.

DORNIER DO 28

Dimensions: Span, 46 ft. 4¾ in.; length, 29 ft. 7¼ in.;
height, 10 ft. 4¾ in.; wing area, 262·3 sq. ft.

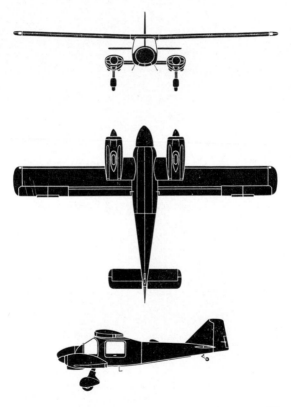

DOUGLAS C-133B CARGOMASTER

Country of Origin: U.S.A.

Type: Heavy Freight and Personnel Transport.

Power Plants: Four Pratt and Whitney T34-P-9W turboprops each rated at 6,500 e.s.h.p. (dry) and 7,500 e.s.h.p. (wet).

Performance: Maximum speed, 359 m.p.h. at 8,700 ft.; initial climb rate, 1,350 ft./min.; service ceiling, 21,300 ft.; range (with 51,845 lb. cargo), 4,030 mls. at 328 m.p.h. at 23,400 ft., (with 77,680 lb. cargo), 1,727 mls. at 325 m.p.h. at 26,850 ft.

Weights: Empty, 120,263 lb.; design loaded, 286,000 lb.; maximum loaded, 300,000 lb.

Development: The C-133B, fifteen examples of which are being delivered to the U.S.A.F., is essentially similar to the C-133A apart from the power plants which were T34-P-3s in the earlier model, and relatively minor changes to the wing and fuselage structure necessitated by the increased power and gross weight. The C-133B features the improved flight deck introduced on the last eight production C-133As, and other changes made on these aircraft, such as enlarged rear loading doors to simplify the loading of Atlas intercontinental ballistic missiles. Thirty-five C-133A Cargomasters were built and one of these has flown with a freight load of 117,900 lb.

DOUGLAS C-133B CARGOMASTER

Dimensions: Span, 179 ft. 7¾ in.; length, 157 ft. 6½ in.; height, 48 ft. 3 in.; wing area, 2,673 sq. ft.

DOUGLAS DC-8 SERIES 40

Country of Origin: U.S.A.

Type: Medium- and Long-range Commercial Transport (116–176 Passengers).

Power Plants: Four Rolls-Royce Conway 507 (R.Co.12) by-pass turbojets each rated at 17,500 lb.s.t.

Performance: Maximum cruising speed (at 220,000 lb.), 590 m.p.h. at 30,000 ft.; range (with 28,336-lb. payload), 6,820 mls. at 551 m.p.h. at 36,000 ft., (with 37,165-lb. payload), 5,100 mls.

Weights: Empty, 130,164 lb.; maximum loaded, 310,000 lb.

Development: The DC-8 is being offered in both domestic and international models, with different power plants and tankages, but all variants produced so far are dimensionally similar. The first DC-8 was flown on May 30, 1958, and eight aircraft were used in the flight test programme, certification of the initial domestic model, the DC-8 Series 10 with 13,500 lb.s.t. Pratt and Whitney JT3C-6 engines, being accomplished on August 31, 1959. The second domestic model is the Series 20 with 15,800 lb.s.t. Pratt and Whitney JT4A-3 turbojets, and the intercontinental models are the Series 30 with 17,500 lb.s.t. JT4A-11 turbojets, the Series 40 described here, and the Series 50 with 17,000 lb.s.t. JT3D-1 or 18,000 lb.s.t. JT3D-3 turbo-fans. The Conway-powered Series 40 was certificated on March 24, 1960, and this version has been delivered to T.C.A., Alitalia, and C.P.A.L. A proposed all-cargo version is designated DC-8A.

94

DOUGLAS DC-8 SERIES 40

Dimensions: Span, 142 ft. 5 in.; length, 150 ft. 6 in.;
height, 42 ft. 4 in.; wing area, 2,771 sq. ft.

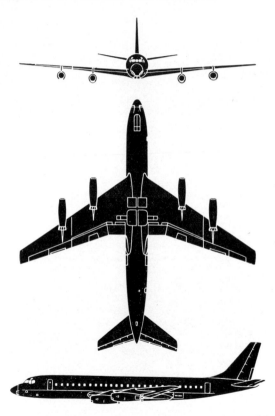

DOUGLAS A4D-2N SKYHAWK

Country of Origin: U.S.A.
Type: Single-seat Shipboard Attack Bomber.
Power Plant: One Wright J65-W-16A single-shaft turbojet rated at 7,800 lb.s.t.
Performance: Maximum speed, 676 m.p.h. at sea level (Mach 0·88); normal combat radius, 460 mls.; maximum range (with external fuel), 1,150 mls.; maximum unrefuelled endurance, 2·75 hr.
Weights: Empty, 9,559 lb.; normal loaded, 17,294 lb.
Armament: Two 20-mm. and three Martin ASM-N-7 Bullpup command-guidance air-to-surface missiles, or up to 5,000 lb. ordnance on three pylons (1,000 lb. on each wing pylon and 3,000 lb. on fuselage pylon). External loads may include a Mk. 11 double-barrelled 20-mm. cannon pack.
Development: Flown for the first time on August 21, 1959, the A4D-2N is the current production model of the Skyhawk, and differs from the A4D-2 in having an improved pilot oxygen system, an autopilot, a larger nose radome housing limited all-weather radar, and certain changes to the cockpit. A proposed version of the Skyhawk powered by an 8,500 lb.s.t. Pratt and Whitney J52 turbojet is designated A4D-5. To be fitted with a ground-level ejection seat, the A4D-5 will have a 27% increase in range over the A4D-2N.
96

DOUGLAS A4D-2N SKYHAWK

Dimensions: Span, 27 ft. 6 in.; length, 40 ft. 1¼ in., (including refuelling probe) 42 ft. 10¾ in.; height, 15 ft.; wing area, 260 sq. ft.

G

DOUGLAS A3D-2 SKYWARRIOR

Country of Origin: U.S.A.

Type: Three-seat Shipboard Attack Bomber (-2P) Five-seat Photographic-reconnaissance, (-2Q) Seven-seat Radar Countermeasures, and (-2T) Eight-seat Bombardier Trainer.

Power Plants: Two Pratt and Whitney J57-P-10 two-spool turbojets each rated at 10,500 lb.s.t. (dry) and 12,400 lb.s.t. (wet).

Performance: (A3D-2) Maximum speed, 610 m.p.h. at 10,000 ft. (Mach 0·83); tactical radius on internal fuel (3,651 Imp. gal.), 1,050 mls.; service ceiling, 41,000 ft.; typical mission endurance, 5·5 hr.

Weights: Empty, 38,298 lb.; normal loaded, 73,000 lb.; maximum loaded, 84,000 lb.

Armament: (A3D-2) Two 20-mm. cannon in Westinghouse tail turret and 12,000-lb. bomb load.

Development: One heavy attack squadron of A3D-2 Skywarriors is based aboard each of the U.S. Navy's principal carriers. Capable of L.A.B.S. bombing with automatic, semi-automatic or manual techniques, the A3D-2 entered service with the U.S. Navy early in 1957. Variants in service in addition to the basic attack bomber model are the A3D-2P (illustrated above) photo-reconnaissance aircraft, the A3D-2Q radar countermeasures-reconnaissance aircraft illustrated by the silhouette) and the A3D-2T bombardier trainer.

98

DOUGLAS A3D-2 SKYWARRIOR

Dimensions: Span, 72 ft. 6 in.; length, 76 ft. 4 in.; height, 22 ft. 9½ in.; wing area, 780 sq. ft.

DOWNER BELLANCA 260 MODEL 14-19-3

Country of Origin: U.S.A.

Type: Four-seat Cabin Monoplane.

Power Plant: One Continental IO-470-F six-cylinder horizontally-opposed engine rated at 260 h.p.

Performance: Maximum speed, 207 m.p.h.; cruising speed (75% power), 203 m.p.h. at 9,000 ft., (65% power), 185 m.p.h.; initial climb rate, 1,750 ft./min.; service ceiling, 22,000 ft.; range (maximum fuel and 15 min. allowances), 880 mls.

Weights: Empty, 1,690 lb.; maximum loaded, 2,700 lb.

Development: The Bellanca 260 produced by the Downer Aircraft Industries (formerly Northern Aircraft) is derived from the Model 14-19-2 Cruisemaster, 104 examples of which were built after the purchase by the company of the Bellanca Aircraft Corporation. The Cruisemaster was powered by a 230 h.p. Continental O-470-K engine and featured a retractable tail-wheel undercarriage, and the Model 14-19-3, or Bellanca 260, differs principally in having a more powerful engine and a nosewheel undercarriage. The prototype Model 14-19-3 flew on November 15, 1958, and the first production aeroplane was delivered on March 6, 1959. More than 200 aircraft of this type have now been delivered and production is currently two per week.

100

DOWNER BELLANCA 260 MODEL 14-19-3

Dimensions: Span, 34 ft. 2 in.; length, 22 ft. 11 in.; height, 6 ft. 4 in.; wing area, 161·5 sq. ft.

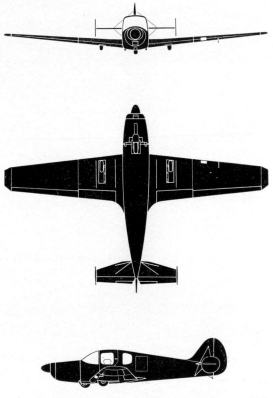

ENGLISH ELECTRIC CANBERRA B.(I).8

Country of Origin: Great Britain.

Type: Two-seat Light Bomber and Intruder.

Power Plants: Two Rolls-Royce Avon 109 single-shaft turbojets each rated at 7,400 lb.s.t.

Performance: Maximum speed, 518 m.p.h. at sea level (Mach 0·68), 580 m.p.h. at 30,000 ft. (Mach 0·83); initial climb rate (at 55,134 lb.) 3,400 ft./min.; maximum operational altitude, 48,000 ft.; maximum range (interdictor with combat allowances), 800 mls. at 403 m.p.h. at 2,000 ft.; maximum ferry range, 3,630 mls.

Weights: Empty, 23,173 lb.; normal loaded (no tip tanks), 50,992 lb., (with tip tanks), 55,134 lb.; maximum loaded, 56,250 lb.

Armament: Four 20-mm. Hispano cannon in optiona ventral pack, two 1,000-lb. bombs internally and two 1,000-lb. bombs externally.

Development: The Canberra B.(I).8 multi-purpose aircraft will remain in R.A.F. service until the mid-'sixties and the arrival of its supersonic successor, the TSR.2. Export version of the Canberra B.(I).8 include the B.(I).12, eleven examples of which have been supplied to the R.N.Z.A.F., and the B.(I).58, sixty-six of which have been delivered to the Indian Air Force. Eight B.(I).8s have been supplied to each of the Peruvian and Venezuelan air arms. Production of the Canberra by the parent company terminated late in 1960 after more than ten years.

ENGLISH ELECTRIC CANBERRA B.(I).8

Dimensions: Span, 63 ft. 11½ in.; length, 65 ft. 6 in.;
height, 15 ft. 7 in.; wing area, 960 sq. ft.

ENGLISH ELECTRIC LIGHTNING F.1

Country of Origin: Great Britain.
Type: Single-seat Day and All-weather Interceptor.
Power Plants: Two Rolls-Royce Avon 200 Series single-shaft turbojets each rated at 11,250 lb.s.t. (dry) and 14,430 lb.s.t. (afterburning).
Estimated Performance: Maximum speed, 1,386 m.p.h. at 40,000 ft. (Mach 2·1); maximum climb rate, 30,000 (plus) ft./min.; service ceiling, 60,000 ft.; endurance, 1·25 (plus) hrs.
Weights: Approximate maximum loaded, 40,000 lb.
Armament: Two or four 30-mm. Aden cannon and two de Havilland Firestreak infra-red homing missiles or forty-eight 2-in. rocket projectiles.
Development: The Lightning F.1 entered service during the course of 1960, the first R.A.F. Squadron to re-equip with this fighter being No. 74 at Coltishall. New marks of the Lightning currently being evolved will be powered by the R.B.146 Avon 300 series engines and will carry later homing missiles. The Lightning T.4 two-seat operational trainer possesses the same specified Mach number as the single-seater and carries a twin-Firestreak pack and Ferranti Airpass radar but has no cannon flanking the cockpit.

ENGLISH ELECTRIC LIGHTNING F.1

Dimensions: Span, 34 ft. 10 in.; length, 50 ft.; height, 19 ft. 5 in.

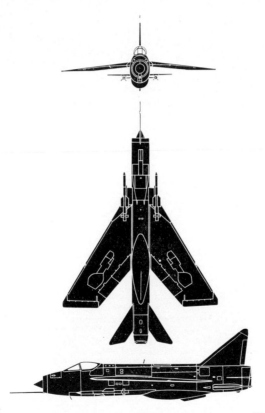

FAIREY GANNET A.E.W.3

Country of Origin: Great Britain.

Type: Three-seat Shipboard Early-warning Aircraft.

Power Plant: One Bristol Siddeley Double Mamba 102 (A.S.M.D.8) double turboprop rated at 3,875 e.h.p.

Performance: Estimated maximum speed, 250 m.p.h. at 5,000 ft.; approximate service ceiling, 25,000 ft.; endurance, 4–5 hr.

Weights: Loaded, 20,000–25,000 lb.

Development: The first Fleet Air Arm unit to receive the Gannet A.E.W.3, No. 849 Squadron, reached full strength during 1960, and a small number of aircraft of this type remained to be delivered at the end of that year. The prototype Gannet A.E.W.3 flying radar control centre flew for the first time on August 20, 1958, and the first production machine flew some three months later, on December 2nd. Initial deck landing trials took place on H.M.S. *Centaur* in November 1958, and on August 18, 1959, the Royal Navy's No. 700G Intensive Flying Trials Flight was formed with Gannet A.E.W.3s, completing 1,855 flying hours with three machines by the end of January 1960. Only some thirty Gannet A.E.W.3s have been ordered.

FAIREY GANNET A.E.W.3

Dimensions: Span, 54 ft. 6 in.; length, 44 ft.; height, 16 ft. 10 in.; wing area, 490 sq. ft.

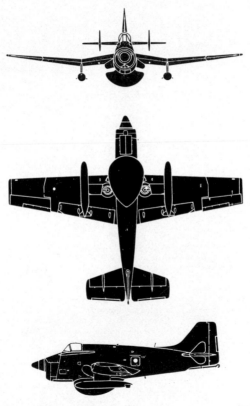

FIAT G.91R

Country of Origin: Italy.

Type: Single-seat Reconnaissance Fighter and Strike Aircraft.

Power Plant: One Bristol Siddeley Orpheus 803 single-shaft turbojet rated at 5,000 lb.s.t.

Performance: Maximum speed, 668 m.p.h. at sea level (Mach 0·88), 675 m.p.h. at 5,000 ft. (Mach 0·9), 637 m.p.h. at 20,000 ft. (Mach 0·91); combat radius (including 10-min. loiter), 196 mls.; cruising speed, 253 m.p.h. up to 35,000 ft.; initial climb rate, 6,000 ft./min.; time to 26,000 ft. 3 min. 45 sec.

Weights: Empty, 6,550 lb.; normal loaded, 11,365 lb.; maximum, 12,500 lb.

Armament: Four 12·7-mm. Colt-Browning machine guns or two 30-mm. cannon, and two 500-lb. bombs, two packs of nineteen or thirty-one 2·75-in. rockets, twelve 3-in. or six 5-in. rockets or four pods each containing one 12·7-mm. gun with 250 r.p.g.

Development: The G.91R is essentially similar to the G.91, the first prototype of which flew on August 9, 1956, apart from cameras in the extreme nose. The G.91 entered service with the Italian 103rd Light Tactical Fighter Squadron in 1959. Fifty are being supplied to West Germany and a further 232 are being manufactured in that country, deliveries commencing in the summer of 1961.

108

FIAT G.91R

Dimensions: Span, 28 ft. 2½ in.; length, 34 ft. 2½ in.; height, 13 ft. 1¼ in.; wing area, 176·74 sq. ft.

FIAT G.91T

Country of Origin: Italy.

Type: Two-seat Basic and Operational Trainer.

Power Plant: One Bristol Siddeley Orpheus 803 single-shaft turbojet rated at 5,000 lb.s.t.

Performance: Maximum speed, 633 m.p.h. at sea level; range (with 444 Imp. gal.), 1,367 mls.; time to 13,120 ft., 4 min. 30 sec., to 26,250 ft., 8 min.; service ceiling, 39,370 ft.

Weights: Empty, 7,275 lb.; normal loaded, 11,794 lb.

Armament: Two 12·7-mm. Colt-Browning machine guns with 250 r.p.g.

Development: Flown for the first time on May 31, 1960, the Fiat G.91T is essentially a tandem two-seat training variant of the basic G.91 single-seat strike fighter, and is currently in production for the Italian and West German air arms, deliveries to the latter service commencing in the spring of 1961. The G.91T is capable of fulfilling most of the roles of the single-seat variant, and the prototype (illustrated here) is, in fact, fitted with three high-speed low-level reconnaissance cameras and two Colt-Browning guns. Various external armament loads may be carried, such as two 500-lb. general-purpose or Napalm bombs, two Nord AS-20 air-to-surface missiles, two pods each containing nineteen or thirty-one 2·75-in. rockets, twelve 3-in. rockets or six 5-in. rockets.

FIAT G.91T

Dimensions: Span, 28 ft. 2½ in.; length, 38 ft. 3¾ in.; height, 13 ft. 11¼ in.; wing area, 176·74 sq. ft.

F.M.A. I.A.-35-II HUANQUERO

Country of Origin: Argentina.

Type: Light Military Transport (Seven passengers).

Power Plants: Two I.A.R.-19A El Indio nine-cylinder air-cooled radials each rated at 628 h.p.

Performance: Maximum speed, 225 m.p.h. at 7,000 ft.; maximum cruising speed, 218 m.p.h. at 9,200 ft.; economical cruising speed, 215 m.p.h. at 11,485 ft.; range (at econ. cruising), 777 mls.; initial climb rate, 1,598 ft./min.; service ceiling, 21,381 ft.

Weights: Empty, 7,717 lb.; loaded, 12,130 lb.

Development: The I.A.-35-II is a light transport version of the Huanquero general-purpose aircraft which has been in production since 1957. The prototype Huanquero flew for the first time on September 21, 1953, but the first production aeroplane did not fly until March 29, 1957. Five basic versions have been developed: the I.A.-35-Ia crew trainer; the I.A.-35-Ib gunnery and bombing trainer; the I.A.-35-II transport illustrated here; the I.A.-35-III ambulance aircraft, and the I.A.-35-IV photographic aircraft. The Huanquero operates successfully from short, semi-prepared airstrips, and an experimental version known as the Constancia II is to be powered by two Turboméca Bastan turboprops.

F.M.A. I.A.-35-II HUANQUERO

Dimensions: Span, 64 ft. 3½ in.; length, 45 ft. 10½ in.;
height, 12 ft. 2 in.; wing area, 452·084 sq. ft.

FOKKER F.27 FRIENDSHIP SERIES 200

Country of Origin: The Netherlands.
Type: Short- and Medium-haul Commercial Transport (32–48 Passengers).
Power Plants: Two Rolls-Royce Dart 528 (R.Da.7) single-shaft turboprops each rated at 2,100 e.h.p.
Performance: Recommended cruising speed at 20,000 ft. (36,000 lb.), 302 m.p.h., (at 34,000 lb.), 307 m.p.h.; range (5% reserves and max. payload: 12,500 lb.), 267 mls., (9,200 lb. payload), 385 mls., (5,000 lb. payload), 1,540 mls.
Weights: Maximum loaded, 37,500 lb.
Development: Friendships powered by the 1,742 e.h.p. Dart 511 (R.Da.6) and the Dart 528 (R.Da.7) are respectively designated Series 100 and Series 200 by the parent company and F-27 and F-27A by the Fairchild company which initiated production of this transport in the U.S.A. in June 1956. The military version, illustrated by the silhouette, is known as the F.27M Troopship, and nine aircraft of this type have been supplied to the Royal Netherlands Air Force together with three F.27 Friendships. With a reinforced floor and cargo loading doors the F.27 is known as the Freightship by Fokker and F-27B by Fairchild. Friendships built by the latter company feature a 17-in. increase in fuselage length, and both companies are considering an S.T.O.L. version, the F.27S, with double-slotted flaps and variable-incidence tailplane.

FOKKER F.27 FRIENDSHIP SERIES 200

Dimensions: Span, 95 ft. 2 in.; length, 75 ft. 9 in.; height, 27 ft. 6 in.; wing area, 754 sq. ft.

FOLLAND GNAT T.1

Country of Origin: Great Britain.
Type: Tandem Two-seat Advanced Trainer.
Power Plant: One Bristol Siddeley Orpheus 100 single-shaft turbojet rated at 4,230 lb.s.t.
Performance: Maximum speed, 627 m.p.h. at 35,000 ft.; maximum Mach number attainable in level flight, Mach 0·97; initial climb rate, 8,000 ft./min.; service ceiling, 48,000 ft.; endurance, 2·25 hr.
Weights: Basic operational, 5,470 lb.; maximum loaded, 8,970 lb.
Armament: The standard production Gnat T. 1has no armament, but streamlined containers may be attached to the fuselage flanks by pylons, these housing a pair of 30-mm. Aden cannon (110 r.p.g.) or two 0·5-in. Colt-Browning machine guns (250 r.p.g.), and various underwing loads may be carried, including two 1,000-lb. bombs, two 500-lb. bombs and two 66 Imp. gal. drop tanks, eighteen 3-in. rockets with 25-lb. warheads, twelve 3-in. rockets with 60 lb. warheads, two rocket pods each containing 24 2-in. rockets or two Firestreak infra-red homing missiles.
Development: The first of fourteen pre-production Gnat trainers ordered in May 1958 flew for the first time on August 31, 1959, and half of this batch had flown by the end of 1960, the remainder being scheduled for completion by May 1961. An initial production batch of thirty machines was ordered during 1960, and these should begin to enter service with R.A.F. Training Command towards the end of 1961, supplanting the de Havilland Vampire T.11.

FOLLAND GNAT T.1

Dimensions: Span, 24 ft.; length, 30 ft. 9 in.; height, 9 ft. 7½ in.; wing area, 175 sq. ft.

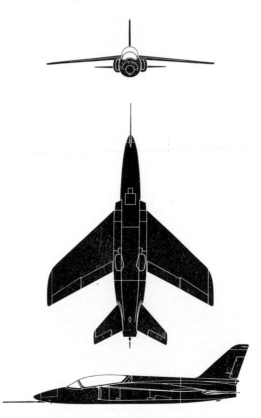

G.A.M. DASSAULT ETENDARD IVM

Country of Origin: France.

Type: Single-seat Shipboard Strike Fighter.

Power Plant: One S.N.E.C.M.A. Atar 8 single-shaft turbojet rated at 9,700 lb.s.t. (dry).

Performance: Maximum speed, 713 m.p.h. at 36,000 ft. (Mach 1·08), 686 m.p.h. at sea level (Mach 0·9); tactical radius at sea level (on internal fuel), 186 mls.; range with two 132 Imp. gal. drop tanks, 500 mls. at 36,000 ft.; climb to 40,000 ft., 4·5 min.; service ceiling, 50,000 ft.

Weights: Normal catapult weight, 19,400 lb.; maximum loaded, 23,000 lb.

Armament: (Interception) One 30-mm. DEFA cannon and four Sidewinder infra-red homing missiles or two Sidewinders and two Nord 5103 beam-riding missiles; (attack) two 1,000-lb. and two 500-lb. bombs or four pods each containing eighteen 68-mm. unguided missiles plus two 30-mm. DEFA cannon.

Development: The delivery of an initial batch of fifty Etendard IVM aircraft to the French Navy is scheduled to commence in November 1961, and it is anticipated that a second batch of fifty will be ordered. The seventh pre-production machine, the Etendard IVF, is a reconnaissance model, and the third machine, the Etendard IVB illustrated above, has an 11,200 lb.s.t. Avon 51 engine and has been adapted for flap blowing.

118

G.A.M. DASSAULT ETENDARD IVM

Dimensions: Span, 31 ft. 6 in.; length, 47 ft. 3 in.;
height, 13 ft. 7⅝ in.; wing area, 306 sq. ft.

G.A.M. DASSAULT MIRAGE III C

Country of Origin: France.

Type: Single-seat Interceptor Fighter and Strike Fighter.

Power Plant: One S.N.E.C.M.A. Atar 9C single-shaft turbojet rated at 9,370 lb.s.t. (dry) and 13,200 lb.s.t. (afterburning), plus one detachable SEPR 841 rocket motor rated at 3,300 lb. thrust for 80 sec.

Performance: Maximum speed, 1,520 m.p.h. at 40,000 ft. (Mach 2·2); economical cruising speed, 595 m.p.h. at 40,000 ft. (Mach 0·9); time to 36,000 ft. (without rocket) 2·3 min., to 50,000 ft., 6·05 min., to 59,000 ft. (with rocket), 5·0 min.; service ceiling (without rocket), 59,000 ft., (with rocket), 75,000 ft.; zoom climb altitude, 100,000 ft.; endurance (single intercept at 60,000 ft.), 21 min.

Weights: Empty, 12,350 lb.; loaded (high-altitude intercept), 18,620 lb., (long-range strike), 22,150 lb., (ferry), 22,860 lb.; maximum, 26,000 lb.

Armament: One Nord 5103 or Matra 511 air-to-air missile, two Sidewinders, or one 1,100-lb. bomb.

Development: One hundred Mirage IIIC interceptors were ordered in September 1958, and the 1960 French Budget authorised the purchase of a further hundred machines including twenty-six Mirage IIIB trainers, making provision for the purchase of a further 270 multi-mission Mirage IIIs by the end of 1965. Both the Australian and Swiss governments were evincing interest in the Mirage III late in 1960. The first production Mirage IIIC flew on October 9, 1960.

G.A.M. DASSAULT MIRAGE III C

Dimensions: Span, 26 ft. 9 in.; length, 43 ft. 10 in.;
height, 14 ft. 0 in.; wing area, 374 sq. ft.

G.A.M. DASSAULT MIRAGE IVA

Country of Origin: France.
Type: Two-seat Medium-range Light Bomber.
Power Plants: Two S.N.E.C.M.A. Atar 9D single-shaft turbojets each rated at approx. 10,800 lb.s.t. (dry) and 14,990 lb.s.t (afterburning).
Performance: Maximum speed, 1,386 m.p.h. at 36,000 ft. (Mach 2·1); tactical radius (flying to target at supersonic speed and returning at Mach 0·9), 800 mls.
Weight: Normal loaded (prototype), 55,100 lb.
Armament: One nuclear weapon recessed beneath the fuselage.
Development: Intended to equip the Armée de l'Air's nuclear strike force, the Mirage IVA will, in its production form, carry anti-missile countermeasures equipment and elaborate navigation and bombing radar. Fifty aircraft of this type have been ordered, seven being scheduled for delivery in 1963, twenty-two in 1964, and the remainder in 1965. Essentially a scaled up Mirage III (see preceding pages), the Mirage IV-01 prototype was flown for the first time on June 17, 1959, and exceeded Mach 2·0 in level flight during December of that year, establishing a 1,000-km. closed circuit record at 1,131 m.p.h. on September 19, 1960. The second prototype, scheduled to fly in the spring of 1961, will have the Atar 9D turbojets proposed for the production model. A larger version, the Mirage IVB powered by Pratt and Whitney J75 turbojets, was abandoned as a result of a reappraisal of the aircraft's mission profile.

G.A.M. DASSAULT MIRAGE IVA

Approximate Dimensions: Span, 37 ft.; length, 67 ft.;
height, 19 ft. 6 in.; wing area, 670 sq. ft.

G.A.M. DASSAULT 410 SPIRALE

Country of Origin: France.
Type: Multi-purpose Military Aircraft.
Power Plants: Two Turboméca Bastan single-shaft turboprops each rated at 935 e.s.h.p.
Performance: Maximum speed (clean), 320 m.p.h., (with external weapons), 295 m.p.h.; maximum cruising speed, 280 m.p.h. at 9,840 ft.; maximum range (internal fuel), 1,554 mls., (with external fuel), 2,176 mls.
Weights: Loaded (attack), 12,346 lb., (liaison), 13,117 lb., (ambulance), 11,420 lb.
Armament: Two 30-mm. DEFA cannon with 200 r.p.g. and six SS-11 guided missiles, four pods each containing eighteen 68-mm. unguided missiles, or two missile pods and two 1,100-lb. bombs.
Development: A non-pressurized military version of the civil M.D.415 Communauté with which it has been developed in parallel, the prototype M.D.410 Spirale was flown for the first time on April 8, 1960. Equipped with low-pressure tyres which permit operation from semi-prepared airfields, the Spirale normally carries two crew members, although an additional crew member is carried for the photo-reconnaissance role. Five passengers may be carried and, for the ambulance role, two casualty litters and medical attendants.

124

G.A.M. DASSAULT 410 SPIRALE

Dimensions: Span, 53 ft. 10¾ in.; length, 42 ft. 7¾ in.;
height, 14 ft. 1¼ in.; wing area, 387·5 sq. ft.

GLOSTER JAVELIN F.A.W.9

Country of Origin: Great Britain.
Type: Two-seat Night and All-weather Interceptor.
Power Plants: Two Bristol Siddeley Sapphire 203/204 single-shaft turbojets each rated at 11,000 lb.s.t. (dry) and 12,300 lb.s.t. (afterburning).
Estimated Performance: Maximum speed, 695 m.p.h. at 10,000 ft. (Mach 0·95), 635 m.p.h. at 35,000 ft.; maximum climb rate, 10,000–12,000 ft./min.; service ceiling, 55,000–60,000 ft.
Weights: Approximate loaded, 38,000 lb.
Armament: Two 30-mm. Aden cannon and four de Havilland Firestreak infra-red homing missiles.
Development: Although production of the Javelin was completed in June 1960, the conversion of Javelin F.A.W.7s to F.A.W.9 standards will continue until July 1961. Whereas the Javelin F.A.W.7 equipped with British radar, was the first variant of the fighter to carry the Firestreak missile and introduced the more powerful Sapphire 200 Series turbojets, the final production model, the F.A.W.8 is fitted with U.S. radar and introduced a simplified system of afterburning, a Sperry autopilot, drooped wing leading edges and dampers on both yaw and pitch axes. The F.A.W.9 is essentially the F.A.W.7 brought up to F.A.W.8 standards but retaining British radar. All Javelins are being equipped for flight refuelling, and the probe which can be attached to the starboard side of the fuselage can be seen in the photo above.

GLOSTER JAVELIN F.A.W.9

Dimensions: Span, 52 ft.; length, 56 ft. 4 in.; height,
16 ft.; wing area, 928 sq. ft.

GRUMMAN G-159 GULFSTREAM

Country of Origin: U.S.A.

Type: Executive Transport (10–12 Passengers) and Feederliner (19 Passengers).

Power Plants: Two Rolls-Royce Dart 529 (R.Da.7/2) single-shaft turboprops each rated at 2,105 e.h.p.

Performance: Maximum cruising speed, 357 m.p.h. at 25,000 ft.; normal cruising speed, 334 m.p.h.; initial climb rate (28,000 lb.), 3,010 ft./min.; service ceiling, 36,900 ft.; maximum range, 2,530 mls. at 300 m.p.h. at 25,000 ft., 1,865 mls. at 260 m.p.h. at 10,000 ft.

Weights: Empty, 18,886 lb.; normal loaded, 31,000 lb.; maximum, 33,600 lb.

Development: Designed specifically for use as an executive transport following an extensive market survey, the Gulfstream was flown for the first time on August 14, 1958, and some sixty aircraft of this type had been manufactured by the end of 1960. Up to twelve passengers can be accommodated, or nineteen in a high-density layout, and all Gulfstreams are furnished to the individual requirements of their owners. The Gulfstream is designed to be completely independent of ground handling facilities, and has its own hydraulically-operated stairway/entrance door, plus an auxiliary power unit for engine starting, etc. The basic Gulfstream structure is adequate to take 2,660 e.h.p. Dart R.Da.10 engines which will provide a 400 m.p.h. cruising speed.

128

GRUMMAN G-159 GULFSTREAM

Dimensions: Span, 78 ft. 4 in.; length, 63 ft. 8¼ in.;
height, 22 ft. 10 in.; wing area, 610·3 sq. ft.

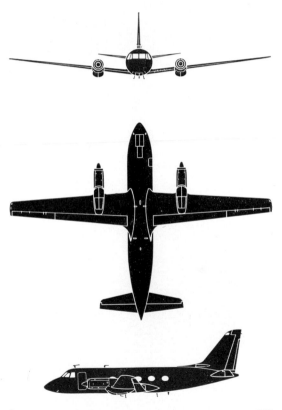

GRUMMAN A2F-1 INTRUDER

Country of Origin: U.S.A.

Type: Two-seat Low-level Shipboard Strike Aircraft.

Power Plants: Two Pratt and Whitney J52-P-6 two-spool turbojets each rated at 8,500 lb.s.t.

Performance: Maximum speed, 685 m.p.h. at sea level (Mach 0·9). No further details available.

Weights: Empty, 24,000 lb.; maximum loaded, 54,000 lb.

Armament: (Typical load) Three 2,000-lb. Mk. 84 bombs and two Martin ASM-7 Bullpup missiles.

Development: Selected from eleven designs submitted by eight manufacturers which participated in a design contest held between May and December 1957 for a low-level shipboard strike aircraft, the A2F-1 Intruder was flown for the first time in April 1960, the initial contract calling for eight machines, four of these having been delivered in 1960. In order to reduce take-off, the A2F-1 is fitted with hinged tailpipes which are tilted 30° by hydraulic actuators to deflect the jet exhaust downward. All weapons are carried externally on five pick-up points, and it is claimed that the A2F-1 can carry a greater and more varied load of stores than any other naval attack aircraft extant. Normal offensive load is some 7,000 lb. Slow flying characteristics are exceptional, and stalling speed with 40° flap, undercarriage extended and full jet deflection is 92 m.p.h.

GRUMMAN A2F-1 INTRUDER

Dimensions: Span, 53 ft.; length, 53 ft. 5 in.; height, 15 ft. 1¾ in.

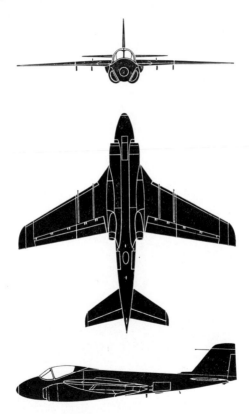

GRUMMAN AO-1BF MOHAWK

Country of Origin: U.S.A.

Type: Two-seat S.T.O.L. Front-line Observation Aircraft.

Power Plants: Two Lycoming T53-L-3 turboprops each rated at 1,005 e.s.h.p.

Performance: Maximum speed, 316 m.p.h. at 5,000 ft.; cruising speed, 230 m.p.h. at 5,000 ft.; initial climb rate, 3,000 ft./min.; service ceiling, 25,000 ft.; normal range, 460 mls.; ferry range (with two 125 gal. drop tanks), 1,670 mls. at 239 m.p.h.

Weights: Empty, 9,028 lb.; maximum loaded, 12,800 lb.

Development: The Mohawk is unique in having been designed to meet a U.S. Army requirement for a short-landing-and-take-off aircraft suitable for front-line use, and the first of nine YAO-1 pre-production machines flew on April 13, 1959. A further seventy-seven production AO-1AF Mohawks have been ordered for the U.S. Army, the first of these being scheduled to enter service during 1961. All Mohawks will carry a complete high resolution optical photographic system as basic equipment, and with S.L.A.R. (side-looking aircraft radar) added (as illustrated) it becomes the AO-1BF. This equipment provides a permanent radar map of the terrain on either side of the aircraft's flight path. With infra-red surveillance equipment the Mohawk is designated AO-1CF. Seventeen each of the -1BF and -1CF are to be delivered. Wing racks can carry camera pods, fuel tanks and a variety of other stores.

GRUMMAN AO-1BF MOHAWK

Dimensions: Span, 42 ft.; length, 41 ft.; height, 12 ft. 8 in.; wing area, 330 sq. ft.

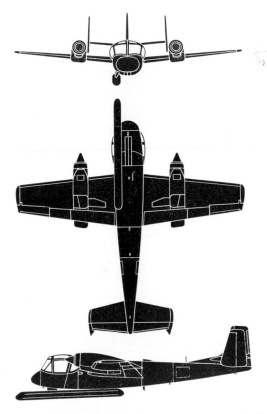

GRUMMAN S2F-3 TRACKER

Country of Origin: U.S.A.

Type: Four-seat Anti-submarine Aircraft.

Power Plants: Two Wright R-1820-82 nine-cylinder air-cooled radials each rated at 1,525 h.p.

Performance: Maximum speed, 280 m.p.h.; patrol speeds, 100–180 m.p.h. at 1,000 ft.; combat radius, 460 mls.; maximum range, 920 mls.; endurance, 8 hrs.

Weights: Approx. empty, 17,000 lb.; normal loaded, 21,000 lb.; maximum, 24,000 lb.

Armaments: Six H.V.A.R. rockets underwing and various internal ordnance loads, including a Mk. 24 mine or Mk. 41 torpedo.

Development: First flown on May 21, 1959, the S2F-3 differs from the S2F-1, currently serving with Canadian, Japanese, Italian and Dutch squadrons as well as the U.S. Navy, in having increased overall dimensions, increased sonobuoy stowage space in each of the engine nacelles (from eight to sixteen sonobuoys), increased fuel capacity and later electronic equipment.

134

GRUMMAN S2F-3 TRACKER

Dimensions: Span, 72 ft. 7 in.; length, 43 ft. 6 in.; height, 16 ft. 7 in.

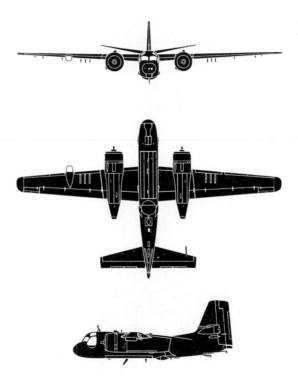

HANDLEY PAGE H.P.R.7 HERALD

Country of Origin: Great Britain.

Type: Short- and Medium-Haul Commercial Transport (44 Passengers).

Power Plants: Two Rolls-Royce Dart 527 (R.Da.7/2) single-shaft turboprops each rated at 2,105 e.h.p.

Performance: Recommended continuous cruising speed 275 m.p.h. at 15,000 ft.; cruising speed for maximum range (6,140 lb. payload), 306 m.p.h. at 23,000 ft.; range (maximum payload), 864 mls., (maximum fuel), 1,727 mls.; initial climb rate, 2,100 ft./min.

Weights: Basic operational, 24,220 lb.; maximum loaded, 39,000 lb.

Development: Flown for the first time on March 11, 1958, the H.P.R.7 Herald is currently in production, and three ordered by the Ministry of Aviation were scheduled to be delivered to British European Airways in January and February 1961. Six Heralds have been ordered by Jersey Airlines with deliveries scheduled to commence in June 1961. These will be 48–50 seaters and will feature an extra 42-in. extension forward of the wing. The manufacturers have obtained letters of intent for sixteen Heralds from airlines in Brazil and Argentina, including one for seven aircraft from the Brazilian operator VASP. These are likely to be of the " stretched " version with the extended fuselage. It is expected that an all-up weight of 40,000 lb. will be approved.

136

HANDLEY PAGE H.P.R.7 HERALD

Dimensions: Span, 94 ft. 4½ in.; length, 71 ft. 11 in.;
height, 23 ft. 4 in.; wing area, 886 sq. ft.

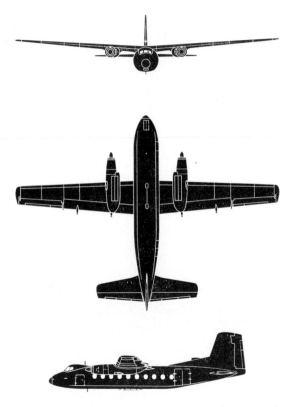

HANDLEY PAGE VICTOR B.2

Country of Origin: Great Britain.

Type: Long-Range Medium Bomber.

Power Plants: Four Rolls-Royce Conway R.Co.11 two-spool by-pass turbojets each rated at 17,250 lb. s.t.

Estimated Performance: Maximum speed, 650 m.p.h. at 40,000 ft. (Mach 0·98); cruising speed, 560–595 m.p.h. (Mach 0·85–0·9) at altitudes up to 55,000 (plus) ft.; normal range (without external fuel and carrying full weapons load), 3,500 (plus) mls.

Weights: Approximate loaded, 160,000–180,000 lb.

Armament: One Avro Blue Steel Mk. 1 rocket-propelled, guided, supersonic-cruise air-to-surface missile or various combinations of nuclear or conventional free-falling weapons.

Development: The original order for Victor B.2s, the first example of which flew on February 20, 1959, was curtailed in August 1960, the official reason being the high cost of converting the bomber to carry the Douglas Sky Bolt. The earlier Victor B.1 has been operational with squadrons of No. 3 Group, R.A.F. Bomber Command since 1958. The Victor B.1 has 11,0000 lb.s.t. Bristol Siddeley Sapphire 202 engines, and its wing span and wing area are 110 ft. and 2,406 sq. ft. respectively.

HANDLEY PAGE VICTOR B.2

Dimensions: Span, 120 ft.; length, 114 ft. 11 in.;
height, 30 ft. 1½ in.; wing area, 2,597 sq. ft.

HAWKER HUNTER F.G.A.9

Country of Origin: Great Britain.

Type: Single-seat Fighter Ground-attack Aircraft.

Power Plant: One Rolls-Royce Avon 207 single-shaft turbojet rated at 10,050 lb.s.t.

Performance: Maximum speed, 715 m.p.h. at sea level (Mach 0·938), 627 m.p.h. at 36,000 ft. (Mach 0·95); time at 46,000 ft., 6·75 min.; absolute ceiling, 53,400 ft.; range (two 230 Imp. gal. and two 100 Imp. gal. drop tanks), 1,854 mls. at 515 m.p.h.; radius of action (with two 1,000-lb. bombs and two 100 Imp. gal. drop tanks), 219 mls. at 1,000 ft., 350 mls. at 39,000 ft.

Weights: Empty, 13,270 lb.; loaded (clean), 17,600 lb.; maximum, 24,000 lb.

Armament: Four 30-mm. Aden cannon and four 1,000-lb. bombs or 100 Imp. gal. Napalm tanks, twenty-four 3-in. rockets or four 2-in. rocket pods.

Development: Derived from the Hunter F.6, the F.G.A.9 flew on July 3, 1959. It differs from the F.6 in having boosted air conditioning with extra oxygen, cutaway flaps and a tail braking chute. All F.G.A.9s are conversions of F.6s as are also photo-reconnaissance F.R. 10s (illustrated by photograph). Some fifty conversions without the extra oxygen are known as the Mk. 6/Interim Mk. 9. The last 88 Swiss Hunter Mk. 58s have been built to F.G.A.9 standards as have also Indian Mk. 56s.

HAWKER HUNTER F.G.A.9

Dimensions: Span, 33 ft. 8 in.; length, 45 ft. 10½ in.; height, 13 ft. 1¾ in.; wing area, 349 sq. ft.

MAX HOLSTE M.H.260 SUPER BROUSSARD

Country of Origin: France.

Type: Light Commercial Transport (17–23 Passengers).

Power Plants: Two Turboméca Bastan single-shaft turboprops each rated at 960 b.h.p

Performance: Maximum continuous cruising speed, 245 m.p.h. at 9,842 ft., 236 m.p.h. at sea level; economical cruising speed, 217 m.p.h. at 9,842 ft.; initial climb rate, 1,673 ft./min.; range (with 45 min. reserves), 621 mls.

Weights: Empty, 9,735 lb.; loaded, 16,975 lb., maximum, 21,164 lb.

Development: The M.H.260 was flown for the first time on July 29, 1960, being preceded, on May 20, 1959, by the M.H.250 with Pratt and Whitney R-1340 piston engines and a shorter fuselage. Four additional pre-production aircraft are scheduled to fly by October 1961, and French government support is being given to a pressurized development, the M.H.262, which will have the same general configuration as the current M.H.260 and will be available for delivery late in 1961. Max Holste will work with Nord Aviation in the production of the Super Broussard, and a production rate of four aircraft per month is scheduled for June 1962.

MAX HOLSTE M.H.260 SUPER BROUSSARD

Dimensions: Span, 71 ft. 8¼ in.; length, 58 ft. 1¼ in.;
height, 20 ft. 11½ in.; wing area, 586·63 sq. ft.

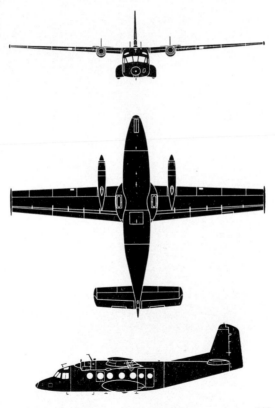

HUNTING JET PROVOST T.4

Country of Origin: Great Britain.

Type: Side-by-side Two-seat Basic Trainer.

Power Plant: One Bristol Siddeley Viper 200 (A.S.V. 11) single-shaft turbojet rated at 2,500 lb.s.t.

Performance: Maximum speed, 380 m.p.h. at sea level, 394 m.p.h. at 10,000 ft., 404 m.p.h. at 20,000 ft., 409 m.p.h. at 30,000 ft.; range, 599 mls. at 20,000 ft., 691 mls. at 30,000 ft.; initial climb rate, 3,340 ft./min.; time to 10,000 ft., 3·75 min., to 20,000 ft., 7·25 min.; endurance, 3·03 hrs. at 25,000 ft.

Weights: Basic operational, 4,707 lb.; maximum loaded, 7,200 lb.

Development: Derived from the Jet Provost T.3 powered by the 1,750 lb.s.t. Viper 102 (A.S.V.8), the Jet Provost T.4 was originally developed as a private venture and, after evaluation by the R.A.F., was ordered in quantity to supplement the earlier model at R.A.F. Flying Training Schools. The more powerful turbojet allows the scope of the basic flying training syllabus employed with the lower-powered Jet Provost T.3 to be extended far beyond the stage previously practicable. An armed export version of the earlier T.3 for the Royal Ceylon Air Force is designated Jet Provost T.51. This is equipped with two 0·303-in. Browning guns and can carry eight 25-lb. bombs and eight Mk. 5 rockets.

144

HUNTING JET PROVOST T.4

Dimensions: Span (over tip tanks), 36 ft. 11 in.; length,
32 ft. 5 in.; height, 10 ft. 2 in.; wing area, 213·7 sq. ft.

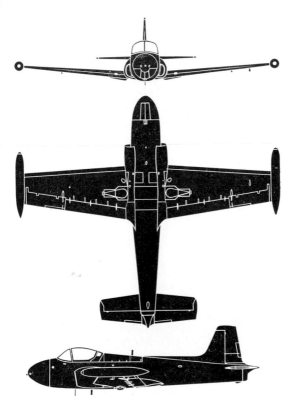

ILYUSHIN IL-18B MOSKVA (COOT)

Country of Origin: U.S.S.R.

Type: Medium-range Commercial Transport (73–111 Passengers).

Power Plants: Four Ivchenko AI-20 single-spoo turboprops each rated at 4,000 e.h.p.

Performance: Cruising speed, 404 m.p.h. at 26,250 ft.; range (with maximum payload: 30,865 lb.), 1,865 mls. at 388 m.p.h. at 26,250 ft.; range (maximum fuel plus one hour reserves), 3,100 mls.

Weights: Empty, 61,730 lb.; maximum loaded, 134,480 lb.

Development: Flown for the first time in June 1957, the IL-18 Moskva is in service with or has been ordered by Aeroflot, C.S.A., Malev, Tarom, the East German Deutsche Lufthansa, and the Communist Chinese airline, and ten aircraft of this type are being supplied to the Ghanaian Air Force. The principal current production version is the IL-18B which accommodates from 73 to 111 passengers. A 120-seat coach model is also available. The first twenty IL-18s were powered alternately by Ivchenko AI-20 and Kuznetsov NK-4 engines of similar output, but the former are now standard. During 1958–59, the IL-18 established a number of F.A.I.-recognised records for speed and altitude with payload.

ILYUSHIN IL-18B MOSKVA (COOT)

Dimensions: Span, 122 ft. 8½ in.; length, 117 ft. 1½ in.; height, 33 ft. 9½ in.; wing area, 1,506·95 sq. ft.

KANPUR-1

Country of Origin: India.

Type: Four-seat Light Cabin Monoplane.

Power Plant: One Lycoming 0-360-A1A four-cylinder horizontally-opposed engine rated at 180 h.p.

Performance: Maximum speed, 129 m.p.h.; cruising speed, 102·5 m.p.h.; range (40 Imp. gal.), 460 mls., (with 20 Imp. gal. auxiliary tank), 650 mls.; initial climb rate, 840 ft./min.; service ceiling, 10,500 ft.

Weights: Empty, 1,700 lb.; loaded, 2,500 lb.

Development: The Kanpur-1 has been designed by Air Vice-Marshal Harjinder Singh of the Indian Air Force Maintenance Command and built at the Kanpur Maintenance Depot. Intended primarily for communications and air observation post duties, the Kanpur-1 is also suitable for use as an air ambulance, as an agricultural aircraft, as a touring monoplane and as a club trainer. All-metal construction is employed with fabric-covered fuselage and control surfaces. As the Kanpur plant is currently tooling up for the licence manufacture of the Avro 748 and 748M transports, it is probable that, if quantity production of the Kanpur-1 is undertaken the light plane will be manufactured by another plant.

KANPUR-1

Dimensions: Span, 37 ft. 10 in.; length, 25 ft. 8 in.; height, 7 ft. 6 in.; wing area, 180 sq. ft.

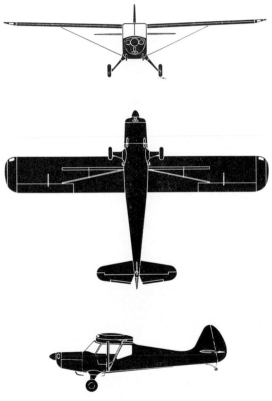

KLEMM KL 107C

Country of Origin: Federal German Republic.
Type: Three-seat Light Cabin Monoplane.
Power Plant: One Lycoming o-320-A2A four-cylinder horizontally-opposed engine rated at 150 h.p.
Performance: Maximum speed, 146 m.p.h.; maximum cruising speed, 127 m.p.h.; economic cruising speed, 121 m.p.h.; range (normal tankage), 510 mls. at 110 m.p.h. at 3,280 ft., (with auxiliary tanks), 870 mls.; initial climb rate, 780 ft./min.; service ceiling, 13,77 ft.
Weights: Empty, 1,377 lb.; normal loaded, 2,137 lb.
Development: Based on a design evolved during the Second World War, the Kl 107 was flown for the first time in 1955, the initial production model being powered by a 90-h.p. Continental engine and designated, Kl 107A. The prototype of a more powerful version the Kl 107 B with a 150-h.p. Lycoming engine flew for the first time on September 4, 1956, and an improved model, the Kl 107C, is currently in production. Owing to the wartime destruction of the Klemm works, the Kl 107C is being manufactured in series by the Bölkow-Entwicklungen. An agricultural model of the Kl 107C is fitted with chemical tanks inboard of the mainwheel legs and spray bars along the wing trailing edges. A more powerful model, the Kl 107D with a 180-h.p. Lycoming, flew for the first time on October 10, 1960.

KLEMM KL 107C

Dimensions: Span, 35 ft. 6¾ in.; length, 27 ft. 2¾ in.; height, 7 ft. 4½ in.; wing area, 157·153 sq. ft.

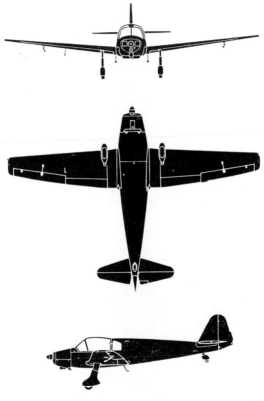

LANCASHIRE PROSPECTOR MK. 1

Country of Origin: Great Britain.

Type: Six-seat Utility and Agricultural Monoplane.

Power Plant: One Lycoming GO-480-G1A6 six-cylinder horizontally-opposed engine rated at 295 h.p.

Performance: Maximum speed, 146 m.p.h. at sea level; max. cruising speed, 128 m.p.h.; econ. cruising, 105 m.p.h. at 2,000 ft.; initial climb rate, 960 ft./min.; service ceiling, 12,500 ft.; range, 580 mls.

Weights: Empty, 2,072 lb.; loaded, 3,700 lb. (agricultural), 4,320 lb.

Development: More than twenty-five Prospector Mk. 1 aircraft have been sold, primarily to agricultural operators, and in the summer of 1960 the prototype of the Mk. 2 version appeared with a 410-h.p. Armstrong Siddeley Cheetah 10 radial engine. This has empty and loaded weights of 2,760 lb. and 4,300 lb. A similar conversion of a Prospector has also been undertaken in Australia. A floatplane version of the Prospector is currently projected.

152

LANCASHIRE PROSPECTOR MK. 1

Dimensions: Span, 43 ft. 6 in.; length, 29 ft. 9 in.; height, 8 ft. 9 in.; wing area, 227·6 sq. ft.

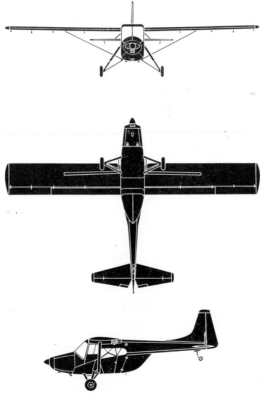

LOCKHEED CL-402 (LA-60)

Country of Origin: U.S.A.

Type: Light Four/six-seat Utility Monoplane.

Power Plant: One Continental TS-IO-470 turbo-super-charged six-cylinder horizontally-opposed engine rated at 260 h.p.

Performance: Maximum speed, 150 m.p.h. at sea level, 165 m.p.h. at 10,000 ft., 167 m.p.h. at 15,000 ft.; economical cruising speed, 130 m.p.h.; range, 550 mls.; initial climb rate, 930 ft./min.; service ceiling, 23,100 ft.

Weights: Empty, 2,024 lb.; normal loaded, 3,532 lb.; maximum, 3,752 lb.

Development: The CL-402, also known as the LASA-60, was flown for the first time on September 15, 1959, and was designed and built at the Georgia Division of the Lockheed Aircraft Corporation to a specification prepared by General Juan Azcarate. The prototype was powered by a 250 h.p. Continental IO-470-G, and production is being undertaken by the Lockheed-Azcarate S.A. at San Luis Potosi, Mexico. It is also to be manufactured in Argentina by Aviones Lockheed-Kaiser, and in Italy by Aeronautica Macchi S.A. The CL-402's S.T.O.L. performance is aided by the installation of high-lift Fowler flaps.

154

LOCKHEED CL-402 (LA-60)

Dimensions: Span, 39 ft. 4 in.; length, 28 ft. 1 in.; height, 10 ft. 8 in.; wing area, 210 sq. ft.

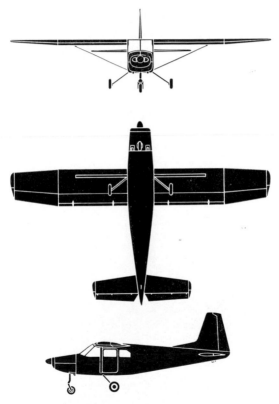

LOCKHEED L.188C ELECTRA

Country of Origin: U.S.A.

Type: Short- and Medium-range Commercial Transport (66–99 Passengers).

Power Plants: Four Allison 501-D13 single-shaft turboprops each rated at 3,750 e.h.p.

Performance: Maximum recommended continuous cruising speed, 405 m.p.h. at 22,000 ft.; range (with maximum payload), 3,450 mls. at 373 m.p.h. at 17,000 ft., (with maximum fuel), 4,430 mls.; normal service ceiling, 27,000 ft.; maximum operating altitude, 30,000 ft.

Weights: Empty, 55,993 lb.; maximum loaded, 116,000 lb.

Development: The L.188 Electra was first flown on December 6, 1957, and the initial production model was the L.188A at a gross weight of 113,000 lb., this being succeeded by the L.188C with extra fuel tankage and a gross weight of 116,000 lb. K.L.M. was the first operator to receive this model. The majority of the Electras ordered had been produced by the end of 1960, but this transport has experienced various difficulties in service. The first fifty-nine Electras were retrofitted in 1959 with modified engine nacelles to reduce airscrew vibration, and wing failures believed to have caused two fatal Electra accidents are necessitating the modification of all aircraft of this type in airline service.

156

LOCKHEED L.188C ELECTRA

Dimensions: Span, 99 ft.; length, 104 ft. 6½ in.; height, 32 ft. 11¼ in.; wing area, 1,300 sq. ft.

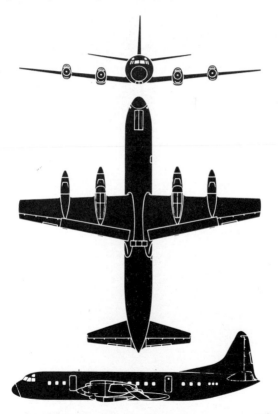

LOCKHEED C-130B HERCULES

Country of Origin: U.S.A.
Type: Medium Multi-purpose Tactical Transport.
Power Plants: Four Allison T56-A-7A single shaft turboprops each rated at 4,050 e.s.h.p.
Performance: Maximum speed, 385 m.p.h.; maximum cruising speed, 370 m.p.h.; econ. cruising speed, 350 m.p.h.; range (22,700-lb. payload), 4,000 mls., (25,000-lb. payload), 3,570 mls. (36,700-lb. payload), 2,450 mls.; initial climb rate, 2,450 ft./min.
Weights: Empty, 67,700 lb.; maximum loaded, 135,000 lb.
Development: The C-130B is a strengthened and more powerful version of the original C-130A, the last example of which was delivered to the U.S.A.F. in February 1959. Twelve C-130A transports were acquired by the R.A.A.F., four C-130Bs were supplied to the R.C.A.F. during 1960, the first of ten C-130Bs for the Indonesian Air Force also being supplied in that year. One machine fitted with an experimental boundary layer control system is designated NC-130B; two rebuilt C-130As for launching target drones are designated GC-130A, and sixteen photographic mapping aircraft are designated RC-130A. The GV-1 is an assault transport version of the C-130B for the U.S. Marine Corps, and a ski-equipped version for the U.S. Navy is designated UV-1L. The SC-130B is a sea-search version for the U.S. Coastguard, and the C-130D for the U.S.A.F. has 3,750 e.s.h.p. T56-A-9 engines and is equipped with skis in addition to wheels.

LOCKHEED C-130B HERCULES

Dimensions: Span, 132 ft. 7¼ in.; length, 97 ft. 8½ in.; height, 38 ft.; wing area, 1,745 sq. ft.

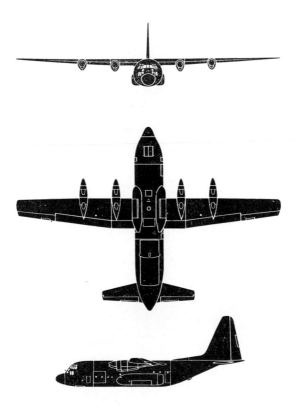

LOCKHEED (C-140) JETSTAR

Country of Origin: U.S.A.

Type: Executive and Utility Transport.

Power Plants: Four Pratt and Whitney JT12A-6 single-shaft turbojets each rated at 3,000 lb.s.t.

Performance: Maximum speed, 573 m.p.h.; recommended continuous cruising speed, 512 m.p.h. at 45,000 ft.; range (2,000-lb. payload and 2,000-lb. reserve fuel), 2,850 mls. at 512 m.p.h. at 45,000 ft.

Weights: Empty, 18,450 lb.; normal loaded, 30,680 lb.; maximum, 38,940 lb.

Development: Designed initially to meet a military requirement for a medium-weight, multi-engined jet utility transport and trainer, the JetStar has also been developed as a business executive aircraft, and the first production aircraft flew in the summer of 1960, the sixth aircraft being the first for a commercial customer, this being scheduled for delivery early in 1961 to the Continental Can Company. Five JetStars have been ordered by the U.S.A.F. under the designation C-140 for use by the Airways and Air Communications Service. These will have larger slipper-type fuel tanks attached to the wings.

LOCKHEED (C-140) JETSTAR

Dimensions: Span, 53 ft. 8 in.; length, 60 ft. 4½ in.;
height, 20 ft. 6 in.; wing area, 543 sq. ft.

LOCKHEED P2V-7 NEPTUNE

Country of Origin: U.S.A.
Type: Long-range Maritime Reconnaissance Bomber.
Power Plants: Two Wright R-3350-32W Turbo Compound engines each rated at 3,500 h.p. and two Westinghouse J34-WE-36 single-shaft turbojets each rated at 3,400 lb.s.t.
Performance: Maximum speed, 403 m.p.h., (piston engines only), 356 m.p.h.; patrol speeds (anti-submarine mission), 173–207 m.p.h. at 1,000 ft.; service ceiling, 22,000 ft.; attainable ceiling, 31,170 ft.; maximum range, 3,685 mls.
Weights: Empty, 49,935 lb.; loaded, 79,895 lb.
Armament: Some P2V-7 Neptunes have two 0·5-in. guns in dorsal turret. Various combinations of mines, depth charges, torpedoes and bombs internally.
Development: The production of the Neptune, originally scheduled to terminate in September 1960, was extended into 1961 by a U.S. Navy order for an additional twenty-six machines. Currently serving with maritime reconnaissance squadrons of Argentina, Australia, Canada, France, Japan, Portugal and the U.S.A. A few serve with the U.S.A.F. as the RB-69, and manufacture is being undertaken in Japan.

LOCKHEED P2V-7 NEPTUNE

Dimensions: Span, 103 ft. 10 in.; length, 91 ft. 8 in.; height, 29 ft. 4 in.; wing area, 1,000 sq. ft.

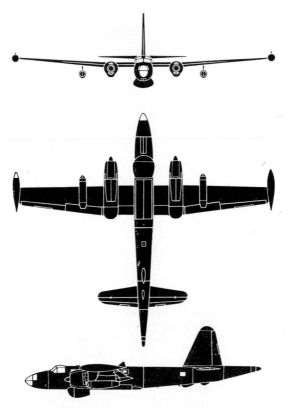

LOCKHEED P3V-1

Country of Origin: U.S.A.

Type: Long-range Maritime Reconnaissance Aircraft.

Power Plants: Four Allison T56-A-10W single-shaft turboprops each rated at 4,585 e.h.p. (wet).

Performance: Approximate maximum speed, 460 m.p.h. at 22,000–24,000 ft.; transit speed (i.e., high speed cruise from base to patrol area), 380–390 m.p.h. at 22,000–24,000 ft.; patrol speed, 220–240 m.p.h. at sea level; patrol endurance (with two engines cut), 8 hours; approx. maximum climb rate, 1,600 ft./min.; sea level climb rate on two engines, 600 ft./min.; service ceiling, 27,000 ft.

Weight: Loaded, 125,000 lb.

Armament: Conventional or nuclear homing torpedoes and depth charges housed in weapons bay and rocket missiles or other weapons on underwing pylons.

Development: Derived from the commercial Electra transport and intended to supplant the P2V-7 in the U.S. Navy from 1961 onwards, the first prototype P3V-1 flew for the first time on November 25, 1959, being preceded on August 29, 1958, by an aerodynamic prototype adapted from an Electra transport. Cruising on the outboard engines only, it is estimated that the P3V-1 can search 370,000 sq. mls. during a single mission.

164

LOCKHEED P3V-1

Dimensions: Span, 99 ft.; length, 113 ft. 7 in.; height, 33 ft. 1 in.; wing area, 1,300 sq. ft.

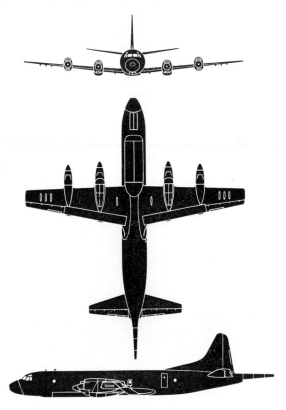

LOCKHEED F-104F STARFIGHTER

Country of Origin: U.S.A.
Type: Two-seat Multi-purpose Combat-proficiency Trainer.
Power Plant: One General Electric J79-GE-7 single-shaft turbojet rated at 10,000 lb.s.t. (dry) and 15,800 lb.s.t. (afterburning).
Estimated Performance: Maximum speed, 1,320 m.p.h. at 40,000 ft. (Mach 2·0); maximum climb rate, 40,000 ft./min.; service ceiling, 60,000 ft.
Weights: Approx. empty, 13,200 lb.; approx. loaded, 22,500 lb.
Armament: Two or four Sidewinder infra-red homing missiles. Provision for one six-barrel rotary-firing 20-mm. Vulcan cannon which, with its ammunition, case and link collector boxes, is interchangeable with a 100 Imp. gal. fuel tank.
Development: Two two-seat variants of the Starfighter are currently in production, the F-104D and F-104F. The former, fully-equipped for operational missions, is derived from the single-seat F-104C and serves with the U.S.A.F. Tactical Air Command and the Nationalist Chinese Air Force. Twenty F-104Ds are being supplied to Japan and twenty to the Netherlands. The F-104F for the Luftwaffe has Martin-Baker upward-ejection seats and equipment generally parallels that of the single-seat F-104G. Thirty have been supplied to Germany.

LOCKHEED F-104F STARFIGHTER

Dimensions: Span, 21 ft. 11 in.; length, 54 ft. 9 in.;
height, 13 ft. 6 in.; wing area, 179 sq. ft.

LOCKHEED F-104G STARFIGHTER

Country of Origin: U.S.A.

Type: Single-seat Interceptor and Fighter-bomber.

Power Plant: One General Electric J79-GE-7 single-shaft turbojet rated at 10,000 lb.s.t. (dry) and 15,800 lb.s.t. (afterburning).

Estimated Performance: Max. speed, 1,520 m.p.h. at 40,000 ft. (Mach 2·3); max. climb rate, 40,000 ft./min.; zoom climb altitude, 90,000 ft.; tactical radius (internal fuel), 400–500 mls.

Weights: Approx. empty, 14,500 lb.; max. loaded, 27,000 lb.

Armament: (Interceptor) One 20-mm. Vulcan rotary cannon and two or four Sidewinder homing missiles.

Development: A multi-mission aircraft derived from the F-104C, the F-104G has been adopted by the R.C.A.F., the Federal German Luftwaffe, and the Dutch and Belgian air arms. Two hundred are being manufactured in Canada as the CF-104 (CL-90), and of 945 expected to be built in Europe, 570 are for West Germany, 200 for the Netherlands, and 100 for Belgium. The similarly-powered F-104C serves with the U.S.A.F. Tactical Air Command, and 180 are to be manufactured in Japan for the J.A.S.D.F. The F-104G differs from the F-104C principally in having a strengthened airframe to permit external loads to be carried at high speeds and low altitudes and withstand increased manœuvrability resulting from the addition of manœuvring flaps, an upward-ejecting seat, and a retractable ventral rocket rail.

168

LOCKHEED F-104G STARFIGHTER

Dimensions: Span, 21 ft. 11 in.; length, 54 ft. 9 in.; height, 13 ft. 6 in.; wing area, 179 sq. ft.

LOCKHEED U-2

Country of Origin: U.S.A.

Type: Single-seat Electronic and Photo Reconnaissance and High-altitude Research Aircraft.

Power Plant: One Pratt and Whitney J57C two-spool turbojet rated at 11,000 lb.s.t. (plus) or one Pratt and Whitney J75-P-13 two-spool turbojet rated at 15,000 lb.s.t. (plus).

Performance: (J57C turbojet) Maximum speed, 495 m.p.h. at 40,000 ft. (Mach 0·75), approx. 200 m.p.h. at sea level; cruising speed, 460 m.p.h. at 40,000 ft. (Mach 0·7); range (653·5 Imp. gal. fuel internally and allowing 12% reserves), 2,200 mls. (with two 87 Imp. gal. pinion auxiliary tanks), 2600 mls. at 460 m.p.h.; maximum ceiling, 70,000–75,000 ft.

Weights: (J57C turbojet) Normal loaded, 15,850 lb.; maximum (with pinion tanks), 17,270 lb.

Development: The U-2 was reputedly designed at the request of the Central Intelligence Agency as an aircraft capable of penetrating far into the Soviet Union at altitudes rendering it immune to interception. Designed in 1954, it is believed that some twenty-five U-2s were built, initial models being powered by the special J57C turbojet and later machines having the more powerful J75-P-13 with which altitudes of the order of 90,000 feet may be attained.

LOCKHEED U-2

Dimensions: Span, 80 ft.; length, 49 ft. 7 in.; approx.
wing area, 675 sq. ft.

MACCHI M.B.326

Country of Origin: Italy.
Type: Tandem Two-seat Basic Training Monoplane.
Power Plant: One Bristol Siddeley Viper A.S.V.11 single-shaft turbojet rated at 2,460 lb.s.t.
Performance: Maximum speed, 507 m.p.h. at 20,000 ft., 495 m.p.h. at 40,000 ft.; cruising speed, 348 m.p.h. at 30,000 ft.; range at cruising speed, 690 mls.; endurance, 2 hr. 7 min.; initial climb rate, 4,420 ft./min.; time to 10,000 ft., 2 min. 36 sec., to 20,000 ft., 5 min. 48 sec., to 30,000 ft., 10 min. 30 sec., to 40,000 ft., 18 min. 30 sec.; service ceiling, 40,000 ft.
Weights: Empty, 5,027 lb.; loaded, 7,430 lb.
Armament: (M.B.326A) Two 7·7-mm. SAFAT machine guns and four 62-lb. rockets or four 100-lb. bombs.
Development: Designed to meet a requirement formulated by the Italian Air Force, the first of two prototypes of the M.B.326 was flown for the first time on December 10, 1957, powered by a 1,750 lb.s.t. Viper A.S.V.8 turbojet. This was supplanted in the second prototype by the more powerful A.S.V.11, and this engine powers the twenty pre-production aircraft, deliveries of which to the Italian Air Force commenced in 1960. Further production orders are currently in process of negotation, and the trainer is being considered by several foreign governments.

MACCHI M.B.326

Dimensions: Span, 32 ft. 11 in.; length, 34 ft. 11¾ in.; height, 11 ft. 7½ in.; wing area, 204·52 sq. ft.

MCDONNELL F4H-1 PHANTOM II

Country of Origin: U.S.A.

Type: Two-seat Shipboard Interceptor and Strike Fighter.

Power Plants: (Development Acft.) Two General Electric J79-GE-2A single-shaft turbojets each rated at 10,350 lb.s.t. (dry) and 16,150 lb.s.t. (afterburning). (Production Acft.) Two J79-GE-8 turbojets each rated at 16,500 lb.s.t. (afterburning).

Performance: Estimated maximum speed, 1,584 m.p.h. at 48,000 ft. (Mach 2·4): range (on internal fuel), 1,500 (plus) mls.; service ceiling, 70,000 ft.; zoom climb altitude, 98,600 ft.

Weight: Loaded, 40,000 (plus) lb.

Armament: Six AAM-N-6 Sparrow III semi-active radar-homing missiles or four Sparrow IIIs and four AAM-N-7 Sidewinder IA infra-red homing missiles. For the strike role conventional or nuclear bombs or air-to-surface missiles may be slung from a fuselage rack and underwing pylons.

Development: Detail specifications for the Phantom II were finalised in July 1955, and the first of twenty-three aircraft for evaluation was flown on May 28, 1958, a total of 192 having been ordered by October 1960. The first forty are powered by the J79-GE-2A but subsequent machines have the J79-GE-8. During trials the Phantom II has attained an altitude of 98,560 ft. in a zoom climb, and in September 1960 this aircraft established a new 500-km. closed-circuit record with a speed of 1,216·78 m.p.h.

MCDONNELL F4H-1 PHANTOM II

Dimensions: Span, 38 ft. 5 in.; length, 58 ft.

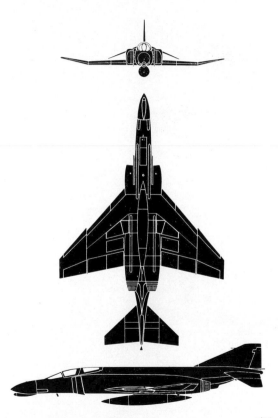

MERCKLE KIEBITZ 501

Country of Origin: Federal German Republic.

Type: Two-seat Utility Monoplane.

Power Plant: One Continental C90-12F four-cylinder horizontally-opposed engine rated at 95 h.p.

Performance: Maximum speed, 102 m.p.h.; minimum speed (flaps down), 31 m.p.h.; normal range, 348 mls.; maximum range (with auxiliary fuel), 600 mls.; service ceiling, 15,750 ft.

Weights: Empty, 990 lb.; loaded, 1,505 lb.

Development: The Kiebitz (Lapwing) has been developed by the Technische Hochschule Branschweig, and the prototype was flown for the first time in October 1959. To be manufactured under licence by the Merckle Flugzeugbau G.m.b.H., the Kiebitz is intended for a wide variety of roles from glider towing to crop dusting, and is of extremely simple construction. Dual controls are fitted and the Kiebitz possesses excellent short take-off-and-landing characteristics, taking off within 82 yards and landing within 44 yards. The immediate predecessor of the Kiebitz was the Zaunkönig, two prototypes of which were built by the same group of engineers at Braunschweig.

MERCKLE KIEBITZ 501

Dimensions: Span, 35 ft. 1¼ in.; length, 22 ft. 4½ in.; height, 6 ft. 9 in.; wing area, 158·983 sq. ft.

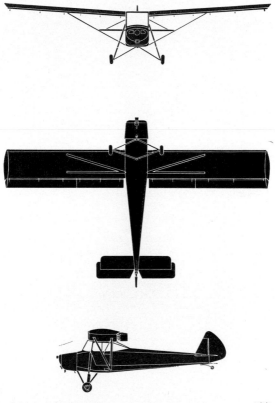

M.F.I. FI 10 VIPAN

Country of Origin: Sweden.

Type: Four-seat Air Observation Post and Utility Monoplane.

Power Plant: One Lycoming 0-320-A1A four-cylinder horizontally-opposed engine rated at 150 h.p.

Performance: Cruising speed (60% power), 122 m.p.h.; initial climb rate, 984 ft./min.; range, 622 mls. at 122 m.p.h.; endurance, 5·1 hr.

Weights: Basic equipped, 1,160 lb.; loaded, 2,200 lb.

Development: The Fi 10 Vipan has been designed and built by the A.B.Malmö Flygindustri (M.F.I.) at Malmö-Bulltofta. Several variants of the Vipan are proposed for both commercial and military applications, and its roles will include those of air observation post, ambulance aircraft, tourer, light utility transport and agricultural aircraft. The M.F.I. has undertaken the development of new reinforced plastics for industrial applications, and plastic sandwich construction is embodied in the Vipan to reduce structural weight. Among several novel features incorporated in the aircraft are a new control system with one-piece or slab-type all-movable tail surfaces, and an all-fibreglass undercarriage.

178

M.F.I. FI 10 VIPAN

Dimensions: Span, 35 ft. 1¼ in.; length, 26 ft. 2½ in.; height, 6 ft.; wing area, 169 sq. ft.

MIG-17 (FRESCO-D)

Country of Origin: U.S.S.R.

Type: Single-seat Day Interceptor Fighter.

Power Plant: One Klimov VK-1A centrifugal turbojet rated at 5,950 lb.s.t. (dry) and 6,990 lb.s.t. (afterburning).

Performance: Maximum speed, 656 m.p.h. at 35,000 ft. (Mach 0·98), 630 m.p.h. at 50,000 ft. (Mach 0·95); combat radius (on internal fuel), 300 mls.; (with external fuel), 725 mls.; maximum range, 1,600 mls.; time to 40,000 ft., 7 min.; service ceiling, 58,000 ft.

Weights: Normal loaded, 13,000 lb.; maximum loaded 14,500 lb.

Armament: Three 23-mm. Nudelmann-Rikter NR-23 cannon and four pods each containing eight 55-mm. rockets, two 210-mm. air-to-ground missiles or two 550-lb. bombs.

Development: Used widely by the air arms of Russia's satellites, and the air arms of Afghanistan, Irak, Indonesia, and the United Arab Republic, the MiG-17 has now been largely supplanted by later types in Soviet first-line units. The Fresco-D, described above and illustrated by the silhouette, differs from the Fresco-C (photograph) in having RP (Scan ODD) interception radar in the nose. The Fresco-A and -B have no radar and an armament of two 23-mm. NR-23 and one 37-mm. N-37 cannon, and the Fresco-E has radar but, like the -A and -B, has no afterburner.

180

MIG-17 (FRESCO-D)

Estimated Dimensions: Span, 36 ft.; length, 38 ft.;
height, 11 ft.

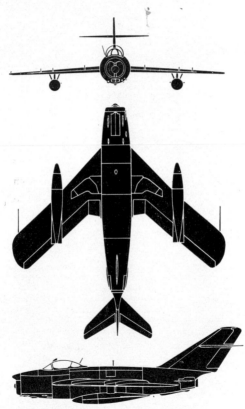

MIG-19 (FARMER-B)

Country of Origin: U.S.S.R.
Type: Single-seat Day and Limited All-weather Interceptor Fighter and Fighter-bomber.
Power Plants: Two Mikulin AM-9b turbojets each rated at 5,500 lb.s.t. (dry) and 7,150 lb.s.t. (afterburning).
Performance: Maximum speed, 740 m.p.h. at 50,000 ft. (Mach 1·125), 860 m.p.h. at 36,000 ft. (Mach 1·3); combat radius (on internal fuel), 290 mls., (with external tanks), 750 mls.; maximum range, 1,700 mls.; time to 50,000 ft., 4·5 min.; service ceiling, 60,000 ft.
Weights: Normal loaded, 17,500 lb.; maximum loaded, 21,000 lb.
Armament: Two 23-mm. Nudelmann-Rikter and one or two 23-mm. cannon in nose (NR-23), and four pods each containing eight 55-mm. air-to-air rockets or two pods each containing nineteen 55-mm. rockets, two 220-mm. or 325-mm. air-to-air missiles.
Development: The first Soviet production nterceptor capable of exceeding Mach unity in level flight, the MiG-19, flew for the first time in 1953 and entered service in 1955. The initial service model (Farmer-A) had AM-5 engines with afterburning thrusts of 6,700 lb., and a lead pursuit optical gun sight. A 37-mm. Nudelmann cannon was carried in the nose. The second model (Farmer-B), illustrated by the silhouette, has RP interception radar (Scan ODD), and a third model (Farmer C) has larger wingroot cannon. A tandem two-seat version has been developed.
182

MIG-19 (FARMER-B)

Estimated Dimensions: Span, 36 ft. 6 in.; length (excluding nose probe), 44 ft. 3 in.; height, 13 ft. 6 in.

NEEFF F.400 COBRA

Country of Origin: Italy.
Type: Two-seat Light Touring and Training Aircraft.
Power Plant: One Turboméca Marboré II turbojet rated at 880 lb.s.t.
Performance: Maximum speed, 379 m.p.h. at 16,400 ft., 360 m.p.h. at sea level; cruising speed, 310 m.p.h. at 13,120 ft.; range, 621 mls. at 14,750 ft.; endurance, 2 hr. 40 min. at 13,120 ft.; service ceiling, 31,100 ft.
Weights: Empty, 1,540 lb.; loaded, 2,860 lb.
Development: The F.400 Cobra has been designed by Ing. Stelio Frati and built by Progetti Construzioni Aeronautiche S.p.A.—Ing. Rico Neeff & C. The Cobra employs a unique form of construction previously used for the F.15 Picchio by the same designer, the skin consisting of a plywood-aluminium laminate, the basic structure being of wood. In addition to increasing the aircraft's resistance to weather, this laminate offers increased strength and rigidity. The first prototype of the Cobra has been completed as a two-seater but the second prototype which was nearing completion at the end of 1960 is a four-seater and the proposed production model will also accommodate four persons. The accompanying silhouette depicts the four-seat second prototype Cobra, and the photograph above illustrates the first prototype.
184

NEEFF F.400 COBRA

Dimensions: Span, 28 ft. 6 in.; length, 25 ft. 6½ in.; height, 9 ft. 2½ in.; wing area, 125·9 sq. ft.

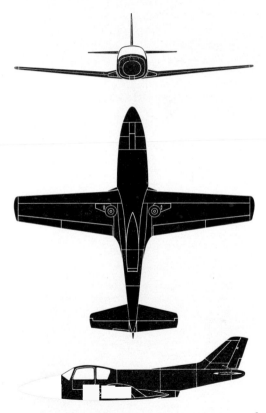

NORTH AMERICAN T2J-1 BUCKEYE

Country of Origin: U.S.A.

Type: Two-seat Shipboard General-purpose Trainer.

Power Plant: One Westinghouse J34-WE-36 single-shaft turbojet rated at 3,400 lb.s.t.

Performance: Maximum speed, 492 m.p.h. at 25,000 ft.; cruising speed, 422 m.p.h. at 39,000–42,200 ft.; range (on internal fuel), 550 mls., (with two 83 Imp. gal. wingtip tanks), 967 mls.; initial climb rate, 5,000 ft./min.; service ceiling, 42,500 ft.

Weights: Empty, 6,893 lb.; normal loaded, 9,916 lb.; maximum loaded, 11,373 lb.

Armament: Two 0·5-in. M-2 machine gun pods, two 100-lb. practice bombs, or two Aero 6A 2·75-in. rocket packs.

Development: The first Buckeye was flown on February 10, 1958, the initial contract calling for the delivery of twenty-six machines, and a follow-on contract was placed on April 20, 1959, the 100th Buckeye being delivered in April 1960. The Buckeye employs a basically similar wing to that of the original FJ-1 Fury fighter, and the basic control system is similar to that of the piston-engined T-28C trainer.

186

NORTH AMERICAN T2J-1 BUCKEYE

Dimensions: Span, 36 ft.; length, 38 ft. 8 in.; height, 14 ft. 9 in.; wing area, 255 sq. ft.

NORTH AMERICAN T-39 (SABRELINER)

Country of Origin: U.S.A.

Type: Utility Trainer and Light Transport.

Power Plants: Two Pratt and Whitney J60 single-shaft turbojets each rated at 2,900 lb.s.t.

Performance: Maximum speed, 595 m.p.h. at 36,000 ft. (Mach 0·9); cruising speed, 500 m.p.h. at 43,600 ft.; normal range, 1,430 mls.; maximum range (with aft fuselage auxiliary tank), 1,725 mls.; initial climb rate, 5,550 ft./min.

Weights: Empty, 9,199 lb.; normal loaded, 15,330 lb.; maximum loaded, 17,760 lb.

Development: The T-39 was designed and built as a private venture to meet the requirements of the U.S.A.F.'s UTX specification which called for an air-craft suitable for providing instruction in jet opera-tional procedures and techniques, night and instrument flying, radar and electronic countermeasures, as well as for tactical mission logistic support. The prototype, powered by two General Electric J85-GE-X turbojets, was flown for the first time on September 16, 1958, and an evaluation quantity of seven T-39s powered by the Pratt and Whitney J60 turbojet was ordered, this being increased to ninety-four aircraft in September 1960. During its initial trials, the first production T-39 flew 1,820 miles non-stop on internal fuel. The T-39 will enter service with the U.S.A.F. during the course of 1961.

NORTH AMERICAN T-39 (SABRELINER)

Dimensions: Span, 44 ft. 4¾ in.; length, 43 ft. 8⅜ in.; height, 15 ft. 10⅞ in.; wing area, 342·5 sq. ft.

NORTH AMERICAN F-100D SUPER SABRE

Country of Origin: U.S.A.
Type: Single-seat Tactical Fighter-bomber.
Power Plant: One Pratt and Whitney J57-P-21A two-spool turbojet rated at 11,700 lb.s.t. (dry) and 16,950 lb.s.t (afterburning).
Performance: Maximum speed, 864 m.p.h. at 35,000 ft. (Mach 1·3); normal range cruise, 565 m.p.h. at 36,000–45,000 ft. (Mach 0·86); combat radius (with 995 Imp. gal. internally and two 229 Imp. gal. drop tanks), 575 mls.; range (with two 375 Imp. gal. external tanks), 1,500 mls.; initial climb rate, 16,000 ft./min.; time to 32,280 ft., 2·5 min.; service ceiling, 51,000 ft.
Weights: Normal loaded, 29,762 lb.; max., 34,832 lb.
Armament: Four 20-mm. M-39E cannon and 7,500-lb. bomb load, two GAM-83A Bullpup air-to-surface or GAR-8 Sidewinder infra-red homing missiles.
Development: Currently serving with the U.S.A.F. Tactical Air Command, the Air National Guard, the Armée de l'Air, and Danish and Turkish air forces, the F-100D was the final single-seat production model of the Super Sabre, 2,294 examples of which (all variants) were built. The F-100F two-seat combat proficiency trainer variant of the F-100D is also in service, and during 1960, eighty of the initial production model, the F-100A, were reconditioned, fitted with F-100D type tail surfaces and Sidewinder launching equipment, and supplied to the Nationalist Chinese.

NORTH AMERICAN F-100D SUPER SABRE

Dimensions: Span, 38 ft. 9½ in.; length (including nose probe), 54 ft. 3 in.; height, 16 ft. 2⅔ in.; wing area, 385·2 sq. ft.

NORTH AMERICAN A3J-1 VIGILANTE

Country of Origin: U.S.A.
Type: Two-seat Shipboard Attack Bomber.
Power Plants: Two General Electric J79-GE-4 single-shaft turbojets each rated at 10,350 lb.s.t. (dry) and 16,150 lb.s.t. (afterburning).
Estimated Performance: Maximum speed, 1,385 m.p.h. at 40,000 ft. (Mach 2·1); normal range, 2,300 mls.; service ceiling, 70,000 ft.; zoom climb altitude, 95,000 ft.
Weight Loaded, 49,500 lb.
Armament: Nuclear or conventional weapons are stored in an axial bay—a tunnel running lengthwise in the aft fuselage—and ejected rearward after the jettisoning of the tail cone.
Development: Flown for the first time on August 31, 1958, the Vigilante is an extremely versatile warplane capable of carrying any store up to a maximum of 6,000 lb. Employing the AN/ASB-11 or -12 radar bombing system, the Vigilante is scheduled to enter service with the U.S. Navy in 1961, some twenty aircraft having flown by the end of 1960. Production Vigilantes will have uprated J79-GE-8 turbojets.

NORTH AMERICAN A3J-1 VIGILANTE

Dimensions: Span, 53 ft.; length, 73 ft.; height, 20 ft.

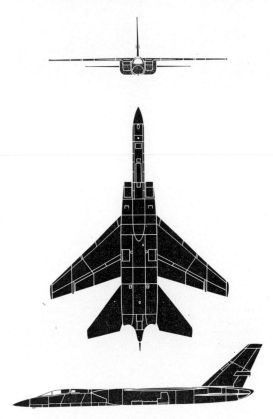

NORTHROP N-156F

Country of Origin: U.S.A.

Type: Single-seat Interceptor Fighter and Fighter-bomber.

Power Plants: Two General Electric J85-GE-5 turbojets each rated at 2,500 lb.s.t. (dry) and 3,850 lb.s.t. with afterburning.

Performance: Maximum speed, 840 m.p.h. at sea level (Mach 1·1), 990 m.p.h. at 40,000 ft. (Mach 1·5); cruising speed, 570 m.p.h. at sea level (Mach 0·75), 560 m.p.h. at 37,500 ft. (Mach 0·85); tactical radius at sea level (with two 125 Imp. gal. drop tanks), 470 mls. at 570 m.p.h., 350 mls. at 686 m.p.h., (at 40,000 ft.), 635 mls.; initial climb rate, 28,000 ft./min.

Weights: Loaded (clean), 12,351 lb.; maximum loaded, 16,112 lb.

Armament: Typical loads: Two Nord AA.25 and two Sidewinder missiles; three Nord AS.30 missiles; two 1,000-lb. and four 500-lb. or 750-lb. bombs; four 0·5-in. gun packs; three 2·75-in. F.F.A.R. packs.

Development: Developed initially as a private venture, the N-156F was flown for the first time on July 30, 1959. The project received U.S. Department of Defence support for three prototypes and a test airframe, and all three aircraft were evaluated at Edwards Air Force Base during 1960. At the time of closing for press, the N-156F had not been chosen as standard equipment by any country, and the production future of the aircraft was doubtful.

194

NORTHROP N-156F

Dimensions: Span, 25 ft. 3 in.; length, 45 ft. 1 in.; height, 13 ft. 1 in.; wing area, 171·15 sq. ft.

NORTHROP T-38A TALON

Country of Origin: U.S.A.

Type: Two-seat Basic Trainer.

Power Plants: Two General Electric J85-GE-5 turbojets each rated at 2,500 lb.s.t. (dry) and 3,850 lb.s.t. with afterburning.

Performance: Maximum speed (at 9,000 lb.), 818 m.p.h. at 36,000 ft. (Mach 1·24); initial climb rate, 28,500 ft./min.; service ceiling, 56,800 ft.; endurance (navigational training mission including 20 min. sea level loiter), 2 hr. 20 min.; range, 1,150 mls.

Weight: Maximum loaded, 11,650 lb.

Development: The first supersonic aircraft designed from the outset for the training role, the Northrop T-38A Talon is scheduled to begin replacing the Lockheed T-33A with the U.S.A.F. Air Training Command during 1961. The first Talon, powered by two non-afterburning YJ85-GE-1 turbojets each rated at 2,100 lb.s.t. was flown on April 10, 1959, a second, similarly-powered machine following on June 12, 1959. The first production T-38A Talon was flown in January 1960 with pre-production YJ85-GE-5 engines each offering an afterburning thrust of 3,600 lb.s.t., but current production models have the 3,850 lb.s.t. (afterburning) J85-GE-5. The Talon is scheduled to enter service at the U.S.A.F.'s Air Training Command Instructors School at Randolph A.F.B. in March 1961, and the first group of students will commence basic training on the type in September 1961. In September 1960, the U.S.A.F. increased its order for Talons from sixty-nine to 213 aircraft.

NORTHROP T-38A TALON

Dimensions: Span, 25 ft. 3 in.; length, 44 ft. 2 in.; height, 12 ft. 10 in; wing area, 170 sq. ft.

OBERLERCHNER JOB 5

Country of Origin: Austria.

Type: Two/three-seat Light Cabin Monoplane.

Power Plant: One Continental C90-12F four-cylinder
horizontally-opposed engine rated at 95 h.p.

Performance: Maximum speed, 112 m.p.h.; cruising
speed, 99 m.p.h.; range, 398 mls.; endurance, 4·1 hr.;
initial climb rate, 787 ft./min.; service ceiling, 18,040 ft.

Weights: (Two-seater) Empty, 944 lb.; loaded, 1,350
lb.; (three-seater) loaded, 1,507 lb.

Development: The first powered aircraft to be produced
by the Josef Oberlerchner company which, founded in
1940, has built some 4,000 gliders, the JOB 5 is of
simple, wooden construction, and work on an initial
production series began in 1959. It is intended that
later production models will be powered by the
Lycoming 0-290-D2B engine of 135 h.p. with which
maximum and cruising speeds of 137 m.p.h. and
121 m.p.h. are anticipated. It is proposed to intro-
duce a fabric-covered steel-tube fuselege, and later
models will be fitted with a nosewheel undercarriage.

OBERLERCHNER JOB 5

Dimensions: Span, 33 ft. 1¾ in.; length, 24 ft. 7¼ in.;
height, 6 ft. 7¾ in.; wing area, 158·229 sq. ft.

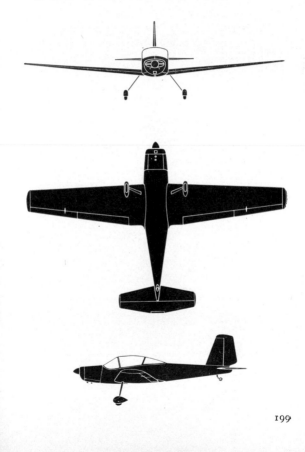

O.K.L. MD-12

Country of Origin: Poland.

Type: Commercial Feederliner (20 passengers).

Power Plants: Four Narkiewicz WN-3 seven-cylinder air-cooled radial engines each rated at 340 h.p.

Performance: Maximum speed, 205 m.p.h. at sea level; cruising speed, 177 m.p.h. at 8,200 ft.; normal range, 435 mls.; maximum range, 745 mls.; initial climb rate, 984 ft./min.; ceiling, 16,400 ft.

Weights: Empty, 10,913 lb.; loaded 16,535 lb.

Development: Flown for the first time in August 1959, the MD-12 feederliner has been built at the Warsaw-Okecie Works of the O.K.L. (Aviation Construction Centre).   Designed by F. Misztal and L. Duleba, the MD-12 has been developed from the twin-engined CSS-12 experimental feederliner, and was originally to have been of twin-engined configuration, but the use of four small engines of indigenous design was decided upon in order to avoid the importation of more powerful foreign engines.   The MD-12 is intended to replace DC-3s (and the Russian-built version of this transport, the Li-2) on the internal routes operated by L.O.T., Poland's national airline, and is of particularly robust construction with simple maintenance characteristics and good short-field performance.   A freighter version featuring two loading doors, one in each side of the rear fuselage, is proposed, this model carrying up to 4,200 lb. of freight.   Ambulance, agricultural and photographic models are also being studied.

O.K.L. MD-12

Dimensions: Span, 69 ft. 10½ in.; length, 51 ft. 8½ in.; height, 19 ft.; wing area, 592 sq. ft.

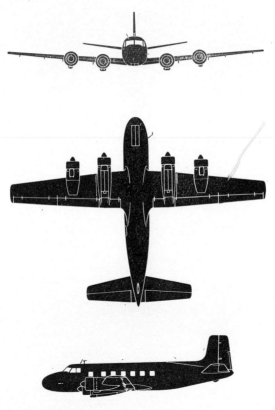

PARTENAVIA P.59 JOLLY

Country of Origin: Italy.

Type: Two-seat Light Touring and Training Monoplane.

Power Plant: One Continental C90-12F four-cylinder horizontally-opposed engine rated at 95 h.p.

Performance: Maximum speed, 121 m.p.h. at sea level; cruising speed (75% power), 109 m.p.h. at sea level; initial climb rate, 690 ft./min.; service ceiling, 16,400 ft.; range at economical cruising speed, 503 mls.

Weights: Empty, 1,058 lb.; loaded, 1,565 lb.

Development: Competing with the Aviamilano P.19 Scricciolo for selection by the Italian Aero Club as a standard club training and touring aircraft, the P.59 Jolly is of mixed construction, the fuselage being a welded steel-tube structure and the wing being a single spar, all-wood structure, the whole being covered by fabric. Side-by-side seating is provided and a fixed nosewheel undercarriage may be fitted in place of the tailwheel undercarriage of the prototype. The P.59 Jolly bears a close family resemblance to the P.57 Fachiro II four-seat touring monoplane, and may be considered a lower-powered development of that aeroplane. No production plans for the Jolly had been announced by the end of 1960.

PARTENAVIA P.59 JOLLY

Dimensions: Span, 30 ft. 2⅛ in.; length, 21 ft. 6¼ in.; height, 6 ft. 11½ in.; wing area, 153·493 sq. ft.

PIAGGIO P.166

Country of Origin: Italy.

Type: Six/eight-seat Light Transport.

Power Plants: Two Lycoming GSO-480-B1C6 six-cylinder horizontally-opposed engines each rated at 340 h.p.

Performance: Maximum speed, 202 m.p.h. at sea level, 226 m.p.h. at 11,000 ft.; cruising speed (70% power), 208 m.p.h. at 12,800 ft., (55% power), 188 m.p.h. at 15,000 ft.; initial climb rate, 1,305 ft./min.; service ceiling, 27,500 ft.; range (6-seat version), 1,155 mls. at 178 m.p.h. at 15,000 ft., (8-seat version), 705 mls.

Weights: Empty (6-seater), 5,070 lb.; loaded, 8,115 lb.

Development: Derived from the P.136-L2 amphibian (known in the U.S.A. as the Trecker Royal Gull Super 200) and employing a similar gull wing and pusher engine installation, the Piaggio P.166 was flown for the first time on November 26, 1957. Known in the U.S.A. as the Trecker 166—Italian manufactured airframes being assembled by the Trecker Aircraft Corporation—the P.166 is one of the roomiest executive transports in its class, and for short-range operations can carry as many as nine passengers. The Italian Air Force has placed an order for 21 P.166 aircraft for communications duties, and aircraft of this type have now been exported to a number of countries, including the United Kingdom, Switzerland, Germany and Australasia.

PIAGGIO P.166

Dimensions: Span, 46 ft. 9. in.; length, 38 ft. $\frac{3}{4}$ in.; height, 16 ft. $4\frac{3}{4}$ in.; wing area, 285·9 sq. ft.

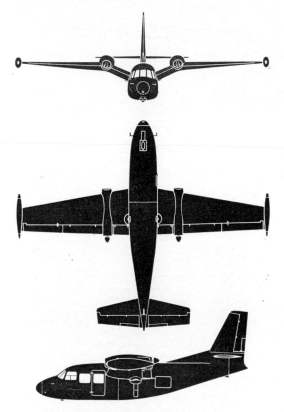

PIPER PA-22 TRI-PACER AND CARIBBEAN

Country of Origin: U.S.A.
Type: Four-seat Cabin Monoplane.
Power Plant: One Lycoming O-320 (-B) four-cylinder horizontally-opposed engine rated at 150 (160) h.p.
Performance: (Figures for Caribbean are quoted in parentheses) Maximum speed, 141 (139) m.p.h.; cruising speed, 134 (132) m.p.h. at 7,000 ft.; range (standard fuel), 536 (528) mls.; initial climb rate, 800 (725) ft./min.; service ceiling, 16,500 (15,000) ft.
Weights: Empty, 1,110 (1,100) lb.; loaded, 2,000 lb.
Development: The PA-22 Tri-Pacer was introduced in 1950 as a development of the 1949 PA-16 Clipper. The first production model, the Tri-Pacer 135 with a 135-h.p. Lycoming O-290O-D2, appeared in February 1951, and in 1953 the power of the Tri-Pacer was increased by 10 h.p. The current production model has the 160-h.p. Lycoming O-320B and the photograph illustrates a 1960 Model Tri-Pacer. In November 1958, a variant of the Tri-Pacer known as the Caribbean was announced and has since been manufactured in substantial quantities. Externally similar to the Tri-Pacer and claimed to be the cheapest four-seater light plane on the U.S. market, the Caribbean has less power than the Tri-Pacer and has been developed specifically for flying club and private owner use.
206

PIPER PA-22 TRI-PACER AND CARIBBEAN

Dimensions: Span, 29 ft. 3½ in.; length, 20 ft. 7¼ in.; height, 8 ft. 3¾ in.; wing area, 147·5 sq. ft.

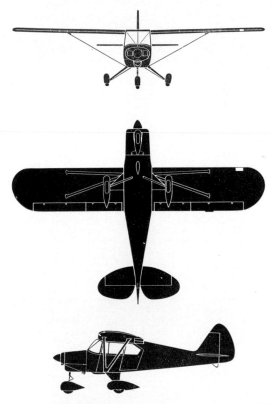

PIPER PA-24 COMANCHE

Country of Origin: U.S.A.

Type: Four-seat Cabin Monoplane.

Power Plant: (PA-24-180) One Lycoming O-360-A1A four-cylinder horizontally-opposed engine rated at 180 h.p. (PA-24-250) One Lycoming 0-540-A1A six-cylinder horizontally-opposed engine rated at 250 h.p.

Performance: (Figures in parentheses refer to the PA-24-250) Maximum speed, 167 (190) m.p.h.; cruising speed (75% power), 160 (181) m.p.h.; range (75% power), 960 (780) mls.; initial climb rate, 910 (1,400) ft./min.; service ceiling, 18,500 (20,000) ft.

Weights: Empty, 1,455 (1,600) lb.; loaded, 2,550 (2,800) lb.

Development: Flown for the first time on May 23, 1956, the Comanche has been in production since 1957, the first production aircraft having flown on October 21st of that year. The Comanche introduced several aerodynamic innovations for aircraft of its class, including laminar flow wings and a one-piece horizontal "flying tail". Both the PA-24-180 and higher-powered PA-24-250 are available in AutoFlite form with Piper AutoControl automatic flight system, and both models are identical aft of the firewall. The photo depicts the 1961 model PA-24-180.

PIPER PA-24 COMANCHE

Dimensions: Span, 36 ft.; length, 24 ft. 8½ in. (24 ft. 10¾ in.); height, 7 ft. 3½ in.; wing area, 178 sq. ft.

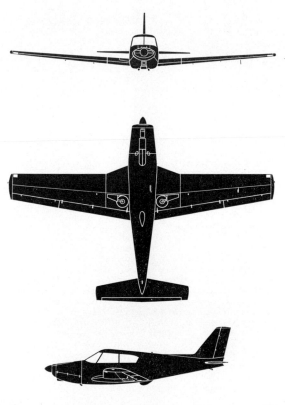

PIPER UO-1 (AZTEC)

Country of Origin: U.S.A.
Type: Five-seat Light Communications Monoplane.
Power Plants: Two Lycoming 0-540 six-cylinder horizontally-opposed engines each rated at 250 h.p.
Performance: Maximum speed, 215 m.p.h.; cruising speed (75% power at 7,000 ft.), 205 m.p.h., (65% power at 9,000 ft.), 200 m.p.h.; normal range (65% power), 1,200 mls.; maximum range (45% power), 1,400 mls.; initial climb rate, 1,650 ft./min.; service ceiling, 22,500 ft.
Weights: Empty, 2,775 lb.; loaded, 4,800 lb.
Development: The UO-1 is the U.S. Navy's version of the Piper Model PA-23-250 Aztec five-seat cabin monoplane, twenty having been ordered in 1960 for communications duties within the continental limits of the U.S.A. The Aztec, which flew for the first time early in 1959, is a development of the PA-23-160 Apache and employs the proven systems and many components of that aircraft. It differs externally from its predecessor in several respects, most obvious of these being the redesigned, swept vertical tail surfaces and the design of the cabin. Deliveries of the Aztec began early in 1960, and apart from communications equipment, the U.S. Navy's UO-1s are identical to the commercial production variant.

PIPER UO-1 (AZTEC)

Dimensions: Span, 37 ft.; length, 27 ft. $7\frac{1}{4}$ in.; height,
10 ft. $3\frac{1}{2}$ in.; wing area, 207 sq. ft.

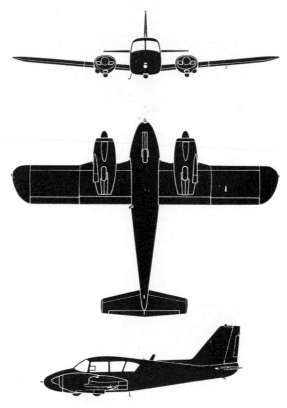

POTEZ-AIR FOUGA C.M.170 MAGISTER

Country of Origin: France.

Type: Tandem Two-seat Basic Trainer.

Power Plants: Two Turboméca Marboré II turbojets each rated at 836 lb.s.t.

Performance: Maximum speed, 403 m.p.h. at sea level, 443 m.p.h. at 30,000 ft.; initial climb rate, 3,350 ft./min.; time to 30,000 ft., 16 min.; service ceiling, 40,000 ft.; range, 576 mls. at 30,000 ft. (with auxiliary tanks), 737 mls.

Weights: Empty, 4,268 lb.; maximum loaded, 6,978 lb.

Armament: Two 7·5-mm. MAC 52 machine guns and two 110-lb. bombs.

Development: More than 400 Magister trainers were in service by the end of 1960, and the licence manufacture of this type is being undertaken in Germany, Israel and Finland, the German, Israeli and Finnish air arms having respectively ordered 250, 44, and 45 machines. In addition, 45 have been ordered for the Belgian Air Force and six for the Austrian Air Force. Thirty examples of a modified version for the French Navy known as the C.M.175 Zéphyr have been delivered, these having sliding cockpit canopies, catapult and arrester gear, and strengthened undercarriages, and an experimental version, the C.M.209, is powered by two 1,058 lb.s.t. Marboré VI turbojets.

212

POTEZ-AIR FOUGA C.M.170 MAGISTER

Dimensions: Span 37 ft. 0⅞ in.; length, 33 ft. 9½ in.;
height, 9 ft. 2¼ in.; wing area, 186,215 sq. ft.

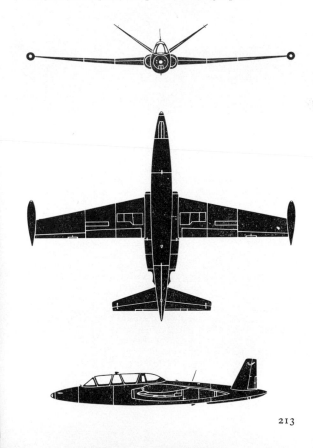

PÜTZER ELSTER-B

Country of Origin: Federal German Republic.
Type: Two-seat Light Cabin Monoplane.
Power Plant: One Continental C90-12F four-cylinder horizontally-opposed engine rated at 95 h.p.
Performance: Maximum speed, 104 m.p.h.; cruising speed, 103 m.p.h.; range at economical cruising speed, 280 mls.; initial climb rate, 720 ft./min.; ceiling, 16,400 ft.
Weights: Empty, 1,012 lb.; loaded, 1,540 lb.
Development: The Alfons Pützer K.G. of Bonn began the development of light powered aircraft by installing a 30-h.p. modified Volkswagen automobile engine in a standard Pützer Doppelraab sailplane to produce the Motorraab. The extensive flight testing of the Motorraab resulted in the evolution of a much improved design, the Elster (Magpie), the prototype of which was powered by a 65-h.p. Porsche 678/1 engine. With the Continental engine, the aircraft was placed in production as the Elster-B, and this type has been selected for use by the Federal German Luftwaffe's sporting flying groups. Suitable for towing sailplanes, the Elster-B has a plywood monocoque fuselage, and the single-spar wings are braced by a streamlined metal strut on each side. Production deliveries of the Elster-B commenced in 1960.

214

PÜTZER ELSTER-B

Dimensions: Span, 43 ft. 4½ in.; length, 23 ft. 3½ in.;
height, 8 ft. 2½ in.; wing area, 188·368 sq. ft.

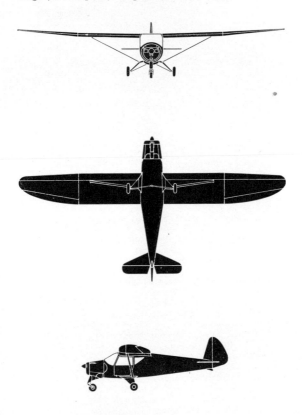

PZL-101 GA

Country of Origin: Poland.
Type: Agricultural Monoplan
Power Plant: One Ivchenko
radial air-cooled engine rated
Performance: Maximum spee
operating speed, 81–87 m.p.h.
rate, 492 ft./min.; ceiling, I
326 mls.
Weights: Empty, 2,119 lb.; lo
Development: The PZL-101 C
developed from the Russian
built in substantial numbers
Warsaw. Evolved by the
struction Centre) at Okecie,
purpose agricultural machine
in two versions, the PZL-101
for agricultural roles, and the
be adapted for freight and
Of mixed construction, the G
from its Russian predecessor,
simplified with a consequent i
The pilot's seat is separated f
by a dustproof fabric curtai
can carry three passengers or
prototype Gawron completed
the Spring of 1958, and it ha
several countries, including I
216

PZL-101 GAWRON

Dimensions: Span, 41 ft. 4½ in.; length, 29 ft. 6½ in.; height, 10 ft. 3 in.; wing area, 256·8 sq. ft.

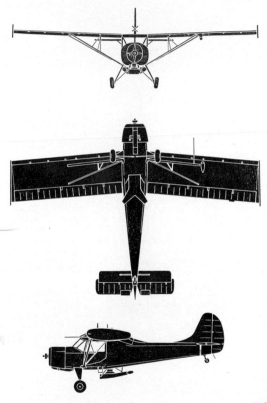

REPUBLIC F-105D THUNDERCHIEF

Country of Origin: U.S.A.

Type: Single-seat All-weather Strike Fighter.

Power Plant: One Pratt and Whitney J75-P-19W two-spool turbojet rated at approximately 17,200 lb.s.t. (dry), 24,500 lb. (afterburning, dry) and 26,500 lb.s.t. (afterburning, wet).

Performance: Maximum speed, 952 m.p.h. at sea level (Mach 1·25), 1,420 m.p.h. at 36,000 ft. (Mach 2·15); initial climb rate (at average gross weight), 34,400 ft./min.; service ceiling, 50,000 (plus) ft.

Weights: Empty, 27,500 lb.; loaded, 35,200–48,400 lb.

Armament: One 20-mm. General Electric T-171E-3 (M-61) Vulcan rotary cannon and up to a maximum of 11,000 lb. of missiles, conventional, nuclear or thermonuclear bombs, or other weapons in 15-ft. weapons bay and on external pylons. Typical external loads for short-range support missions are 190 70-mm. missiles in five pods, or four 1,000-lb. bombs.

Development: The F-105D is the current production version of the Thunderchief, and was first flown on June 9, 1959. The earlier F-105B, seventy-five examples of which were built, differed in having a J75-P-5 turbojet offering a maximum afterburning thrust of 23,500 lb., and was intended primarily for day operations. In addition to the 220 F-105D Thunderchiefs funded for production in the 1960 Fiscal Year, U.S.A.F. plans call for the delivery of a further 1,205 machines by the end of the 1964 Fiscal Year.

REPUBLIC F-105D THUNDERCHIEF

Dimensions: Span, 34 ft. 11 in.; length, 64 ft. 3 in.;
height, 19 ft. 8 in.; wing area, 385 sq. ft.

RHEIN RF-1

Country of Origin: Federal German Republic.
Type: Six-seat S.T.O.L. Light Transport.
Power Plants: Two Lycoming O-540-A1A six-cylinder horizontally-opposed engines each rated at 250 h.p.
Performance: (Estimated) Maximum speed, 180 m.p.h.; cruising speed, 160 m.p.h.; initial climb rate (at 5,072 lb.), 1,452 ft./min., (at 5,955 lb.), 1,146 ft./min.; service ceiling (5,072 lb.), 21,600 ft., (5,955 lb.), 20,300 ft.; normal range (30 min. reserves), 465 mls.; normal endurance, 3·5 hrs.
Weights: Basic, 3,970 lb.; maximum loaded, 5,955 lb.; payload, 1,985 lb.
Development: Flown for the first time during the Summer of 1960, the RF-1 can take off in 360 ft. at a loaded weight of 5,072 lb. and in 502 ft. at a weight of 5,955 lb. Its two Lycoming engines are buried in the wing and drive a single ducted pusher airscrew aft of the cabin. A channel wing forms the lower part of the airscrew duct in which there are slipstream deflection flaps, and an automatic clutch operated by a centrifugal governor and freewheel enable the independent operation of the engines. In the case of a failure of one of the power plants this is automatically declutched with no adverse effect on the symmetry of the flight attitude. The structure of the RF-1 is primarily of metal but considerable use is made of glass-reinforced plastics.

RHEIN RF-1

~nsions: Span (including tip tanks), 46 ft. 3 in.;
~th, 43 ft.; height, 12 ft. 8 in.

SAAB-35B DRAKEN

Country of Origin: Sweden.
Type: Single-seat All-weather Interceptor Fighter and
Fighter-bomber.
Power Plant: One Svenska Flygmotor-built Rolls-
Royce RB.146 Avon 300 Series single-shaft turbojet
rated at 13,220 lb.s.t. (dry) and (approx.) 18,000 lb.s.t.
(afterburning).
Performance: Estimated maximum speed, 1,450 m.p.h.
at 40,000 ft. (Mach 2·2); initial climb rate, 50,000
ft./min.; service ceiling, 60,000 (plus) ft.
Weights: Loaded (without external ordnance), 17,600
lb.; maximum (with two 1,100-lb. bombs), 19,800 lb.
Armament: Two 30-mm. cannon and two or four
Sidewinder infra-red homing missiles (Rb 324), two
pods each housing nineteen 7·5-cm. rockets, eighteen
13·5-cm. Bofors air-to-ground rockets, nine 220-lb.,
four 550-lb., or two 1,100-lb. bombs.
Development: The SAAB-35B (J 35B) Draken is a pro-
gressive development of the SAAB-35A which entered
service with the Flygvapnet in 1960. Equipped with
SAAB S7 collision-course fire-control equipment, the
SAAB-35B differs from the A-model principally in
the type of engine installed, the earlier variant having
an RM 6 (licence-built Avon Series 200) rated at
11,250 lb.s.t. (dry) and 15,190 lb.s.t. (afterburning),
this offering a maximum speed of Mach 1·8 and an
initial climb rate of 39,400 ft./min. A tandem two-
seat training model, the SAAB-35C which was first
flown on December 30, 1959, is similar to the SAAB-
35A apart from the forward fuselage.

INDEX OF AIRCRAFT TYPES

Printed in Great Britain by
Butler and Tanner Ltd., Frome and London
890.1060

SAAB-35B DRAKEN

Dimensions: Span, 30 ft. 9⅞ in.; length (including probe), 51 ft. 10 in.; height, 12 ft. 10 in.; wing area, 538 sq. ft.

SAAB-91D SAFIR

Country of Origin: Sweden.
Type: Four-seat Civil and Military Trainer.
Power Plant: One Lycoming O-360-A1A four-cylinder horizontally-opposed engine rated at 180 h.p.
Performance: (At 2,660 lb.). Maximum speed, 165 m.p.h. at sea level; cruising speed (75% power), 146 m.p.h.; range (66% power), 660 mls. at 5,000 ft.; initial climb rate, 800 ft./min.; service ceiling, 16,400 ft.
Weights: Empty, 1,870 lb.; loaded, 2,660 lb.
Development: The Safir has been produced in four basic models since the prototype flew on November 20, 1945. The initial model, the SAAB-91A, was powered by a 145-h.p. Gipsy Major X, and 16 trainers of this type were delivered to the Ethiopian Air Force and several were acquired by the Flygvapnet as Tp 91 liaison monoplanes. The SAAB-91B, which appeared in 1951, differed primarily in having a six-cylinder Lycoming O-435-A of 190 h.p., and 75 were delivered to the Flygvapnet as the Sk 50, 16 were delivered to Ethiopia and 25 to Norway (SAAB-91B-2). Whereas the A and B models were three-seaters, the SAAB-91C was a four-seater with a similar engine to the B model. Ten of these were purchased by Ethiopia and 14 by the Flygvapnet. The SAAB-91D has a smaller engine than that of the C model and the Finnish and Tunisian air arms have respectively purchased 30 and 15 trainers of this type. The Safir is also used by civil schools in the Netherlands, France, Indonesia and Germany.

SAAB-91D SAFIR

Dimensions: Span, 34 ft. 9 in.; length, 26 ft. 4 in.;
height, 7 ft. 2⅔ in.; wing area, 146 sq. ft.

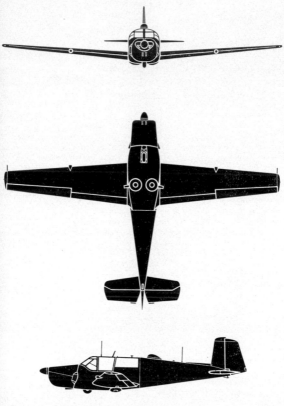

S.A.N. JODEL D.140 MOUSQUETAIRE

Country of Origin: France.
Type: Four-seat Light Cabin Monoplane.
Power Plant: One Lycoming O-360-A2A four-cylinder horizontally-opposed engine rated at 180 h.p.
Performance: Maximum speed, 161 m.p.h.; cruising speed, 140–143 m.p.h.; initial climb rate, 985 ft./min.; service ceiling, 14,760 ft.; range (with maximum fuel), 808 mls. at 141 m.p.h.; maximum endurance, 6 hrs.
Weights: Empty, 1,323 lb.; loaded, 2,535 lb.
Development: The D.140 Mousquetaire is a four-seater based on the popular two-seat Jodel series and developed by the Société Aéronautique Normande (S.A.N.) which company had previously manufactured the side-by-side two-seat Jodel D.117 Grand Tourisme (production of which was handed over to the Société Alpavia at the end of 1958) and the Jodel DR.100 Ambassadeur three-seater. The prototype Mousquetaire flew for the first time on July 4, 1958, and fourteen aircraft had been delivered by the end of that year. Only thirty Mousquetaires were delivered in 1959 as components for some seventy machines were lost in a fire at the Bernay factory, but a production rate of 10–12 aircraft per month was attained during the course of 1960. The Mousquetaire is of wooden construction, and the rear seat can accommodate three passengers with a reduction in the normal baggage allowance from 205 lb. to 44 lb.

226

S.A.N. JODEL D.140 MOUSQUETAIRE

Dimensions: Span, 33 ft. 5½ in.; length, 25 ft. 11 in.; height, 7 ft.; wing area, 193·75 sq. ft.

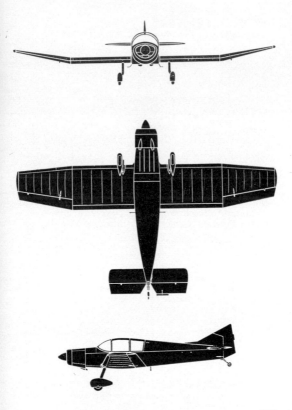

SCHEIBE SF-23A SPERLING

Country of Origin: Federal German Republic.
Type: Two-seat Light Cabin Monoplane.
Power Plant: One Continental C90-12F four-cylinder horizontally-opposed engine rated at 95 h.p.
Performance: Maximum speed, 124 m.p.h.; maximum cruising speed, 109 m.p.h.; range, 435 mls.; endurance, 4 hr.; climb to 3,280 ft., 4 min.; service ceiling, 21,325 ft.
Weights: Empty, 926 lb.; loaded, 1,455 lb.
Development: The Sperling (Sparrow) was designed by Dipl. Ing. Egon Scheibe and was flown for the first time on August 8, 1955 with a 65-h.p. Continental engine. A side-by-side two-seater derived from the series of sailplanes produced by the Scheibe-Flugzeugbau, the prototype Sperling was extensively tested before the monoplane was placed in production with a more powerful Continental engine, the first production machine flying in September 1958. Suitable for instructional purposes and capable of towing sailplanes up to 1,100 lb. in weight, the Sperling is of fabric-covered steel-tube construction and is stressed for aerobatics. Continental engines of 85 h.p. or 65 h.p. or the 65-h.p. Porsche may be fitted as alternatives to the C90-12F.

SCHEIBE SF-23A SPERLING

Dimensions: Span, 32 ft. 4½ in.; length, 20 ft. 4 in.;
height, 7 ft. 1¾ in.; wing area, 130·899 sq. ft.

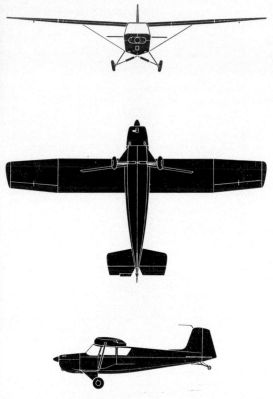

SCINTEX CP.301C ÉMERAUDE

Country of Origin: France.
Type: Two-seat Light Cabin Monoplane.
Power Plant: One Continental C90-12F or -14F four-cylinder horizontally-opposed engine rated at 90 h.p.
Performance: Maximum speed, 130 m.p.h. at sea level; cruising speed (75% power), 112 m.p.h. at sea level, 121 m.p.h. at 4,920 ft.; initial climb rate, 590 ft./min.; service ceiling, 13,120 ft.; range, 620 mls.
Weights: Empty, 871 lb.; loaded, 1,433 lb.
Development: The CP.301C Émeraude manufactured by Scintex-Aviation S.A. is a development of the Piel CP.30 designed by Claude Piel and flown for the first time in 1952 with a 65-h.p. Continental engine. With a 90-h.p. Continental engine and various refinements, the CP.30 became the CP.301A, the B and C models differing in minor details only. The Émeraude is being manufactured by several French concerns, including the Ateliers Aéronautiques de la Côte d'Émeraude and the Société Ouest Constructions Aéronautiques, but the principal manufacturer is Scintex who have evolved a four-seat version, the ML.145 Rubis. The Garland Aircraft Company plan to produce an anglicised model of the Émeraude as the Garland Linnet, and the type is produced under licence in Germany by Schemp-Hirth, and in South Africa by General Aircraft (Pty) Ltd. as the Genair Aerial 2. More than five hundred Émeraude cabin monoplanes have now been built.

SCINTEX CP.301C ÉMERAUDE

Dimensions: Span, 27 ft. o¾ in.; length, 20 ft. 1 in.; height, 5 ft. 10¾ in.; wing area, 118·4 sq. ft.

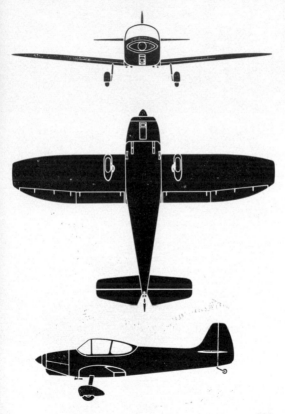

SCOTTISH AVIATION TWIN PIONEER SERIES 3

Country of Origin: Great Britain.

Type: Light General-purpose Transport (16–19 passengers).

Power Plants: Two Alvis Leonides 531/8B nine-cylinder air-cooled radials each rated at 640 h.p.

Performance: Maximum continuous cruising speed, 158 m.p.h. at 2,500 ft.; economical cruising speed, 134 m.p.h. at 5,000 ft.; initial climb rate, 1,250 ft./min.; ceiling (at 14,600 lb.), 21,250 ft.; maximum range (with 2,550-lb. freight), 576 mls.

Weights: Basic operational, 10,062 lb.; maximum loaded, 14,600 lb.

Development: More than 130 Twin Pioneers are in service with operators in some twenty countries, and the current production model is the Series 3 which is basically similar to the Series 1 (550-h.p. Leonides 514/8 engines) apart from the power plants. The Series 2 has Pratt and Whitney R-1340 engines. Thirty-six aircraft basically similar to the Series 1 have been supplied to the R.A.F. as the Twin Pioneer C.C.1, and three have been supplied to the Royal Malayan Air Force.

SCOTTISH AVIATION TWIN PIONEER
SERIES 3

Dimensions: Span, 76 ft. 6 in.; length, 45 ft. 3 in.; height, 12 ft. 3 in.; wing area, 670 sq. ft.

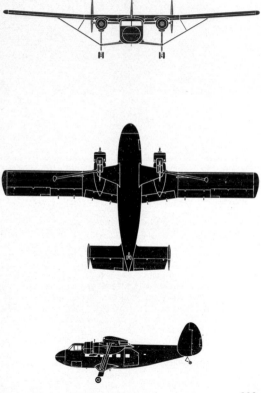

SHORT SC.1

Country of Origin: Great Britain.
Type: Single-seat Vertical Take-off and Landing
Research Aircraft.
Power Plants: Four Rolls-Royce RB.108 turbojets for
lift each rated at 2,130 lb.s.t., and one RB.108 for
forward propulsion rated at 2,300 lb.s.t.
Performance: Level speeds of the order of 230 m.p.h.
have been attained during tests.
Weights: Maximum weight for vertical take-off, 7,800
lb., for oblique take-off, 8,000 lb.
Development: The Short SC.1 research aircraft made
its first transition from normal wing-borne flight to
stationary jet-lift hovering and back again on April 6,
1960.   The first British flat-rising jet-lift aircraft, the
SC.1 was flown for the first time as a conventional
aeroplane on April 2, 1957, and the first untethered
vertical take-off was accomplished on October 25, 1958.
To generate lift four of the RB.108 turbojets are
arranged in two swivelling pairs pointing downwards
and tilting to facilitate transition from hovering to
forward flight.   At low forward speeds stabilisation
and control of the aircraft are effected by two pairs
of downwards-facing air nozzles, one pair located at
the extremities of the fuselage and the other pair
located beneath the outer wings.

SHORT SC.1

Dimensions: Span, 23 ft. 6 in.; length (including probe),
29 ft. 10 in.; height, 9 ft. 10 in.; wing area, 141·9 sq. ft.

SUD-AVIATION SE-210 CARAVELLE 3

Country of Origin: France.
Type: Short/medium-range Transport (80 passengers).
Power Plants: Two Rolls-Royce Avon 527 (R.A.29/3) single-shaft turbojets each rated at 11,700 lb.s.t.
Performance: Maximum continuous cruising speed, 500 m.p.h. at 32,800 ft.; maximum cruising altitude, 39,370 ft.; range (maximum payload: 16,755 lb.), 1,750 mls. at 473 m.p.h.; maximum range (8,100-lb. payload), 2,645 mls.
Weights: Empty, 57,970 lb.; maximum loaded, 99,208 lb.
Development: Some seventy Caravelles had been completed by the end of 1960, and of these thirty-five were Caravelle 1s powered by 10,500 lb.s.t. Avon 522 turbojets. The current production Caravelle 3 differs solely in having higher-powered Avons, and the Caravelle 6, deliveries of which were scheduled to commence early in 1961, has still more powerful Avon 531s rated at 12,500 lb.s.t., permitting an increase in maximum take-off weight to 103,620 lb. The Caravelle 7 and 8 are respectively versions powered by the 16,100 lb.s.t. General Electric CJ805-23 and the 14,340 lb.s.t. Rolls-Royce RB.141/3, and the Caravelle 14 is to be fitted with a new wing of Douglas design and RB.141/11A engines of 15,000 lb.s.t. Apart from the new wing, the Caravelle 14 will have a stretched fuselage to permit ninety-five passengers to be carried over a range of some 2,190 miles.

SUD-AVIATION SE-210 CARAVELLE 3

Dimensions: Span, 112 ft. 6½ in.; length, 105 ft. 0¼ in.; height, 28 ft. 7⅓ in.; wing area, 1,579 sq. ft.

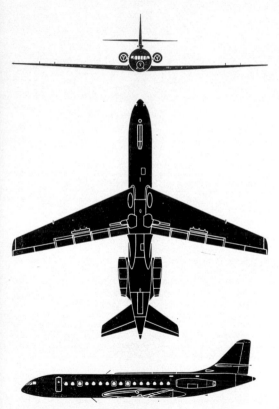

TUPOLEV TU-104B (CAMEL)

Country of Origin: U.S.S.R.
Type: Medium-range Commercial Transport (100 passengers).
Power Plants: Two Mikulin RD-3M turbojets each rated at 15,000 lb.s.t.
Performance: Maximum speed, 614 m.p.h. at 30,000 ft. (Mach 0·91); maximum cruising speed, 560 m.p.h. at 32,800 ft. (Mach 0·85); range cruising speed, 500 m.p.h. at 32,800–39,400 ft.; range (maximum payload), 1,860 mls.; maximum range, 2,485 mls.
Weights: Maximum payload, 26,455 lb.; approximate maximum loaded, 166,000 lb.
Development: The Tu-104B was the third version of the basic design to enter service with Aeroflot. The Tu-104 flew for the first time on June 17, 1955, and entered service with Aeroflot on September 15, 1956, carrying 50 passengers. The second version, the Tu-104A, provided accommodation for 70 passengers, and 3 aircraft were purchased by the Czech national airline, C.S.A. The Tu-104A, like the original Tu-104, has an overall length of 126 ft. 3¾ in. and maximum loaded weight is 166,450 lb. The third version to enter service, the Tu-104B, featured a 3·9 ft. increase in fuselage length. A new variant, the Tu-104E with more powerful engines, established a new record in 1960 by carrying 22,046 lb. over 1,243 mls. at 596·12 m.p.h.

238

TUPOLEV TU-104B (CAMEL)

Dimensions: Span, 113 ft. 3¾ in.; length, 130 ft. 3 in.;
height, 39 ft. 4½ in.; wing area, 2,023·61 sq. ft.

TUPOLEV TU-114 (CLEAT)

Country of Origin: U.S.S.R.

Type: Long-range Commercial Transport (170–220 passengers).

Power Plants: Four Kuznetsov NK-12 single-shaft turboprops each rated at 8,000–9,000 s.h.p.

Performance: Maximum cruising speed, 495 m.p.h. at 32,800 ft.; normal range cruise, 450 m.p.h. at 30,000 ft.; normal range, 6,000 mls.; maximum range, 9,000 mls.

Weights: Normal loaded, 370,000 lb.; maximum loaded, 400,000 (plus) lb.

Development: The largest commercial transport in the world at the present time, the Tu-114 was flown for the first time in the Autumn of 1957 and entered production in 1959. Unexpected teething troubles encountered at a late stage in the test programme, including difficulties with the Kuznetsov engines, have delayed its introduction on scheduled Aeroflot services, however, and it is unlikely to appear regularly on the 4,300-mile Moscow–Khabarovsk and other long-stage Aeroflot routes until the early summer months of 1961. During 1960, the Tu-114 established a number of international records by flying 3,107 mls. with a 55,116 lb. load at an average speed of 544·7 m.p.h. The Tu-114 employs the wings, undercarriage and much of the tail assembly of the Tu-20 (Bear) bomber, and the engines are derated versions of those employed by the bomber. The Tu-114D is a civil counterpart of the Tu-20 which, unlike the Tu-114 described and illustrated here, retains the basic bomber fuselage.

TUPOLEV TU-114 (CLEAT)

Dimensions: Span, 212 ft.; length, 177 ft.; height, 13 ft. 9½ in.; wing area, 3,347 sq. ft.

TUPOLEV TU-124

Country of Origin: U.S.S.R.
Type: Medium-range Commercial Transport (44–68 passengers).
Power Plants: Two Soloviev turbofan engines of unspecified thrust.
Performance: Maximum speed, 620 m.p.h.; average cruising speed, 560 m.p.h. over stages up to approximately 920 mls. at 33,000 ft.; take-off run (at unspecified weight), 2,630 ft.
Weights: No details available for publication.
Development: The Tu-124, the prototype of which appeared early in 1960 and which is now in quantity production for use by Aeroflot on express inter-city services, is the first Russian transport aeroplane to be powered by turbofan engines. Designed by A. A. Arkhangelskii, a senior member of the Tupolev design bureau, the Tu-124 closely follows the earlier Tu-104 in general appearance, although its overall dimensions are considerably smaller. The wing leading edges and air intake duct lips are sharper than those of the larger transport owing to the Tu-124's higher cruising speeds, and exceptional short take-off qualities are attributed to the transport. Three versions are proposed, one having accommodation for 44–46 first-class passengers, another being an economy-class model with accommodation for 68 passengers, and a third being a tourist-class model carrying 55–60 passengers.

TUPOLEV TU-124

Dimensions: No details available for publication.

VEB-152-II

Country of Origin: German Democratic Republic.
Type: Medium-range Commercial Transport (48–72 passengers).
Power Plants: Four Pirna 014 turbojets each rated at 6,950 lb.s.t.
Performance: Maximum speed, 571 m.p.h. at 15,400 ft.; cruising speed, 497 m.p.h. at 30,200–35,400 ft.; initial climb rate (102,530 lb.), 4,330 ft./min.; range, (48 passengers) 1,552 mls., (57–72 passengers), 1,242 mls.
Weights: Empty (48 passengers), 62,060 lb., (57 passengers), 62,370 lb., (72 passengers), 62,660 lb.; maximum loaded, 102,530 lb.
Development: Developed by the Flugzeugwerke Dresden, the VEB-152 is currently in production and has been ordered by the East German Deutsche Lufthansa and the Polish national airline L.O.T. The first prototype VEB-152 was flown on December 4, 1958, and the tenth airliner of this type was scheduled to be completed by the end of 1960, these including six prototypes, three pre-production VEB-152-I aircraft and the first VEB-152-II. The thrust of the turbojets is being increased to 7,270 lb.s.t. in the Pina 014A-1 version but difficulties with this engine have delayed production deliveries of the airliner.

244

VEB-152-II

Dimensions: Span, 86 ft. 7¼ in.; length, 107 ft.; height, 29 ft. 6 in.; wing area, 1,485 sq. ft.

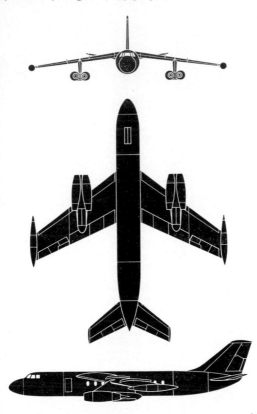

VICKERS VANGUARD II

Country of Origin: Great Britain.
Type: Short- and Medium-range Commercial Transport (76–139 passengers).
Power Plants: Four Rolls-Royce Tyne 512 (R.Ty.11) two-spool turboprops each rated at 5,545 e.h.p.
Performance: Maximum cruising speed, 450 m.p.h.; high speed cruise, 415 m.p.h. at 15,000 ft.; range cruise, 410 m.p.h. at 25,000 ft.; range (maximum fuel), 3,130 mls., (maximum payload), 1,830 mls.
Weights: Basic operational, 85,500 lb.; maximum take-off, 146,500 lb.
Development: Scheduled to enter regular service with B.E.A. early in 1961, the introduction of the Vanguard was delayed some six months by a fault in the compressor of the Tyne engine. The Vanguard flew for the first time on January 20, 1959, and the first of six V.951 Vanguards for B.E.A. flew on April 22, 1959. These are powered by 4,985 e.h.p. Tyne R.Ty.1 turboprops, but sixteen additional machines for B.E.A. are V.953 Vanguard IIs with more powerful turboprops and maximum take-off weight increased from 135,000 lb. to 146,500 lb. Twenty-three basically similar V.952 Vanguard IIs are being delivered to Trans-Canada Airlines. Several variants of the Vanguard are being studied, including freighters with and without rear-loading doors and carrying payloads up to 64,000 lb.
246

VICKERS VANGUARD II

Dimensions: Span, 118 ft.; length, 122 ft. 10⅜ in.;
height, 34 ft. 11 in.; wing area, 1,529 sq. ft.

VICKERS VALIANT B.K.1

Country of Origin: Great Britain.
Type: Long-range Medium Bomber.
Power Plants: Four Rolls-Royce Avon 204 single-shaft turbojets each rated at 10,050 lb.s.t.
Performance: (At 140,000 lb.). Maximum speed, 567 m.p.h. at 30,000 ft. (Mach 0·84), 414 m.p.h. at sea level; maximum cruising speed, 553 m.p.h. at 30,000 ft. (Mach 0·82); economical cruising speed, 495 m.p.h. at 36,000 ft. (Mach 0·75); initial climb rate, 4,000 ft./min.; service ceiling, 54,000 ft.; maximum range, (without external fuel and carrying a 10,000-lb. bomb load halfway) 3,450 mls., (with underwing tanks), 4,500 mls.
Weights: Empty, 75,881 lb.; loaded, 140,000 lb.; max. overload, 175,000 lb.
Armament: Various combinations of nuclear and conventional free-falling weapons up to 10,000 lb.
Development: The first of the R.A.F.'s V-class bombers, the Valiant flew for the first time on May 18, 1951, entering service with No. 138 Squadron early in 1955, and subsequently equipping Nos. 7, 49, 90, 148, 207, 214 and 543 Squadrons. One hundred and four Valiants were built plus three prototypes, the last production Valiant, a B.K.1, flying on August 27, 1957. An experimental model, the Valiant B.2, attained 552 m.p.h. at sea level during trials.

VICKERS VALIANT B.K.1

Dimensions: Span, 114 ft. 4 in.; length, 108 ft. 3 in.;
height, 32 ft. 2 in.; wing area, 2,362 sq. ft.

VICKERS V.810 VISCOUNT

Country of Origin: Great Britain.

Type: Short- and Medium-range Commercial Transport (52–75 passengers).

Power Plants: Four Rolls-Royce Dart 525 (R.Da.7) single-shaft turboprops each rated at 1,990 e.h.p.

Performance: Recommended continuous cruising speed, 351 m.p.h. at 20,000 ft.; range (maximum fuel), 1,760 mls. at 334 m.p.h. at 24,000 ft., (maximum payload), 1,200 mls.

Weights: Empty, 41,276 lb.; maximum loaded, 72,500 lb.

Development: Although series production of the Viscount terminated in 1959, a small number of aircraft were supplied during 1960, customers being Austrian Airlines, All Nippon Airways and Ghana Airways, bringing the total number of Viscounts sold to 429 aircraft. The V.840 is a conversion of the V.810 to take Dart 541 (R.Da.10) engines rated at 2,350 e.h.p. which will offer a 400-m.p.h. cruising speed. The first stretched version of the Viscount, the V.800, was 3 ft. 10 in. longer than the V.700-series Viscounts and was powered by 1,740 e.h.p. Dart 510s. The V.806 was an interim version for B.E.A. with 1,890 e.h.p. Dart 520s, and the V.810 is structurally strengthened to cater for a higher landing weight. Viscounts have been ordered by fifty-four operators in thirty-four different countries.

VICKERS V.810 VISCOUNT

Dimensions: Span, 93 ft. 8½ in.; length, 85 ft. 8 in.;
height, 26 ft. 9 in.; wing area, 963 sq. ft.

VICKERS-SUPERMARINE SCIMITAR F.1

Country of Origin: Great Britain.

Type: Single-seat Shipboard Day Fighter and Strike Aircraft.

Power Plants: Two Rolls-Royce Avon 202 single-shaft turbojets each rated at 11,250 lb.s.t.

Estimated Performance: Maximum speed, 710 m.p.h. at 10,000 ft. (Mach 0·97); radius of action (on internal fuel), 200–250 mls.; maximum climb rate, 10,000–12,000 ft./min.; ceiling, 50,000 ft.

Weights: Normal loaded, 33,000–35,000 lb.; approximate maximum, 40,000 lb.

Armament: Four 30-mm. Aden cannon and (interception) forty-eight 2-in. unguided missiles in underwing pods, or (strike) four 500-lb. or 1,000-lb. bombs or twenty-four 3-in. rockets.

Development: Serving with Nos. 800, 803, 804 and 807 Squadrons of the Royal Navy, the Scimitar is officially credited with nuclear weapons capability. Flown for the first time on January 20, 1956, the Scimitar is equipped for in-flight refuelling and, with nine internal fuel tanks augmented by four 250 Imp. gal. external tanks, can undertake standing air patrols. Approximately one hundred Scimitars had been delivered when production terminated in September 1960.

252

VICKERS-SUPERMARINE SCIMITAR F.1

Dimensions: Span, 37 ft. 2 in.; length, 55 ft. 4 in.; height, 15 ft. 3 in.

CHANCE VOUGHT F8U-2N CRUSADER

Country of Origin: U.S.A.

Type: Single-seat Shipboard Interceptor Fighter.

Power Plant: One Pratt and Whitney J57-P-20 two-spool turbojet rated at 18,000 lb.s.t. (afterburning).

Performance: Maximum speed, 1,300 m.p.h. above 36,000 ft. (Mach 1·97); maximum climb rate, 25,000 (plus) ft./min.; service ceiling, 55,000–60,000 ft.; tactical radius on internal fuel, 300 mls.

Weight: Approximate normal loaded, 29,000 lb.

Armament: Four 20-mm. cannon and two or four AAM-N-7 Sidewinder IA infra-red homing missiles.

Development: A limited all-weather development of the F8U-2 day interceptor, the F8U-2N features increased internal fuel capacity, revised instrumentation and interior and exterior lighting systems, new and more powerful search and tracking radar, and a Vought-developed autopilot to enable it to perform a semi-automatic all-weather mission. The first F8U-2N was delivered to the U.S. Navy on June 1, 1960, by which time more than 700 earlier models of the Crusader had been delivered to the U.S. Navy and U.S. Marine Corps. The immediate predecessor of the F8U-2N, the F8U-2, is powered by the J57-P-16 offering an afterburning thrust of 16,900 lb.

CHANCE VOUGHT F8U-2N CRUSADER

Dimensions: Span, 35 ft. 8 in.; length, 54 ft. 3 in.; height, 15 ft. 9 in.

AER LUALDI L.59

Country of Origin: Italy.

Type: Four-seat Light General-purpose Helicopter.

Power Plant: One Continental IO-470-D six-cylinder horizontally-opposed engine rated at 260 h.p.

Performance: Maximum speed, 99 m.p.h.; cruising speed, 86 m.p.h.; maximum climb rate, 820 ft./min.; hovering ceiling (out of ground effect), 5,575 ft.; absolute ceiling, 19,355 ft.; endurance, 3 hr. 30 min.

Weights: Empty, 1,477 lb.; loaded, 2,557 lb.

Dimensions: Rotor diameter, 34 ft. 9½ in.; fuselage length, 29 ft. 9½ in.; overall height, 9 ft. 8 in.

Development: The Lualdi L.59 is a four-seat development of the two-seat L.55 and L.57 helicopters, and two prototypes have been built by the Macchi factory at Varese. The L.59, like its predecessors, incorporates the "Rotor-Matic" type of rotor system evolved by the Hiller Helicopter Corporation, and this is supplemented by a Lualdi gyroscopic system which is claimed to ensure smoother flight and easier handling qualities. The L.59 features automobile-type doors and can accommodate two casualty litters. It is proposed to build an initial series of fifty production machines.

256

BELL MODEL 47G-3

Country of Origin: U.S.A.

Type: Three-seat Utility Helicopter.

Power Plant: One Franklin 6VS-335 six-cylinder horizontally-opposed engine rated at 225 h.p.

Performance: Maximum cruising speed, 105 m.p.h. at sea level; maximum speed at 15,000 ft., 110 m.p.h.; hovering ceiling (in ground effect), 18,500 ft.; service ceiling, 23,000 ft.; maximum range, 236 mls.; maximum endurance, 3 hr.

Weights: Empty, 1,539 lb.; loaded, 2,550 lb.

Dimensions: Rotor diameter, 37 ft. 3 in.; fuselage length, 28 ft. 6 in.; overall height, 9 ft. 3½ in.

Development: Flown for the first time on July 2, 1959, the Model 47G-3 is a development of the Model 47G-2 Trooper, from which it differs principally in having a greater rotor diameter, a lengthened tail boom and a supercharged engine. Production deliveries of the Model 47G-3 commenced in March 1960, and it is possible to convert the earlier Model 47G-2 to G-3 configuration by means of a modification kit. The Model 47G-2 is designated H-13H Sioux by the U.S. Army. Many Model 47G-2 helicopters have been exported to foreign air arms, one of the latest purchasers being the Brazilian Air Force which acquired twelve in 1960.

BELL HU-1A IROQUOIS

Country of Origin: U.S.A.
Type: Six-seat Utility Helicopter.
Power Plant: One Lycoming T53-L-1 free turbine derated to 770 s.h.p.
Performance: Maximum speed, 142 m.p.h.; cruising speed, 115 m.p.h.; maximum inclined climb rate, 2,100 ft./min.; hovering ceiling (in ground effect), 14,400 ft.; normal range, 186 mls.
Weights: Empty, 3,834 lb.; loaded, 5,800 lb.
Dimensions: Rotor diameter, 44 ft.; fuselage length 39 ft. 7½ in.; overall height, 10 ft. 7 in.
Development: The Bell Model 204, or HU-1A Iroquois, is currently in production for the U.S. Army, deliveries of 110 machines ordered in March 1959 having commenced in April 1960. A variant designated RH-2 (illustrated) is used to test high resolution radar which enables the pilot to see obstacles ahead of the helicopter, and an improved version, the HU-1B, has a T53-L-5 turbine rated at 960 s.h.p. and wider chord main rotor blades of honeycomb construction. A commercial version, the Model 204B, is powered by a 1,100 s.h.p. T53-L-9 turbine, and a manufacturing licence for this version of the helicopter had been acquired by the Italian Agusta company.
258

BOEING-VERTOL YHC-1A CHINOOK

Country of Origin: U.S.A.

Type: Medium Tactical Transport Helicopter.

Power Plants: Two General Electric T58-GE-6 free turbines derated to 825 s.h.p.

Performance: Maximum speed, 172 m.p.h.; maximum cruising speed (90% power), 145 m.p.h.; normal range (10% reserves and 3,000-lb. payload), 230 mls.; maximum range (no reserves), 390 mls.

Weights: Empty, 9,100 lb.; loaded, 15,550 lb.

Dimensions: Rotor diameter (each), 48 ft. 4 in.; fuselage length, 44 ft. 3½ in.; overall height, 17 ft. 7½ in.

Development: Derived from the commercial Model 107-II, the first of three Boeing-Vertol YHC-1A helicopters was flown on August 27, 1959, and these are serving as development machines for the larger YHC-1B which, powered by two 1,940 s.h.p. Lycoming YT55-L-5 turbines, is scheduled to fly early in 1961. Five YHC-1B Chinooks are currently on order for the U.S. Army, and it is expected that a further five will be acquired for the evaluation programme. The YHC-1B has a rear-loading ramp and will carry 33 fully-equipped troops or 24 casualty litters at mission speeds of the order of 150 m.p.h.

259

BÖLKOW BÖ-103

Country of Origin: Federal German Republic.
Type: Single-seat Light Helicopter.
Power Plant: One ILO three-cylinder two-stroke engine rated at 40–50 h.p.
Performance: (Estimated) Maximum speed, 87 m.p.h.; cruising speed, 71 m.p.h.; maximum range, 280 mls.; endurance, 4 hr.
Weight: Loaded, 882 lb.
Dimensions: Rotor diameter, 21 ft. 7 in.
Development: The Bö-103 light helicopter has been derived from the Bö-102 Heli-Trainer fixed-base helicopter trainer, five examples of which have been delivered to the German Army. Eventually to be powered by an 85-h.p. piston engine of unspecified type, the Bö-103 retains most of the features of the Bö-102, and the fuselage is a simple steel-tube structure, the pilot's seat being partly enclosed by a transparent plastic and fibreglass fairing. The three-cylinder engine drives single-blade main and tail rotors, and the main rotor blade, which is of glass-bonded plastic with a foam core, is balanced by a large counter-weight, and has a twin-paddle stabilising bar.

BRANTLY B-2

Country of Origin: U.S.A.
Type: Two-seat Light General-purpose Helicopter.
Power Plant: One Lycoming VO-360-A1A four-cylinder horizontally-opposed engine rated at 180 h.p.
Performance: Maximum speed, 100 m.p.h.; maximum climb rate, 1,580 ft./min.; hovering ceiling (with ground effect), 4,700 ft.; service ceiling, 10,400 ft.; range, 300 mls.
Weights: Empty, 980 lb.; loaded, 1,600 lb.
Dimensions: Rotor diameter, 23 ft. 11¼ in.; fuselage length, 19 ft. 4 in.; overall height, 6 ft. 11¾ in.
Development: The side-by-side two-seat B-2 was flown for the first time on February 21, 1953, and entered production in 1959, some seventy machines having been delivered by the end of 1960. Five B-2 helicopters have been delivered to the U.S. Army for evaluation under the designation YHO-3BR. Although the B-2 can be equipped for agricultural purposes, it is intended primarily as an executive or private owner type. A stressed-skin all-metal fuselage with a conical tail section provide the B-2 with exceptionally clean lines. The three-blade main rotor is of all-metal construction with articulated inboard flapping hinges and drag hinges near mid-span.

FAIRCHILD-UMBAUGH U-18

Country of Origin: U.S.A.

Type: Two-seat Light Gyroplane.

Power Plant: One Lycoming O-360 four-cylinder horizontally-opposed engine rated at 180 h.p.

Performance: Maximum speed, 126 m.p.h.; cruising speed (65% power), 100 m.p.h.; maximum climb rate, 1,050 ft./min.; service ceiling, 15,000 ft.; absolute ceiling, 17,000 ft.; range, 360 mls.; endurance, 3·5 hr.

Weight: Maximum loaded, 1,800 lb.

Dimensions: Rotor diameter, 35 ft.; approx. fuselage length, 25 ft.; approx. overall height, 11 ft. 6 in.

Development: The Umbaugh U-18 two-seat gyroplane is being manufactured in quantity by the Fairchild Engine and Airplane Corporation. The Lycoming engine drives a pusher airscrew and the three-blade rotor is pre-rotated for vertical take-off. The rotor and control systems are extremely simple, having swashplate control for the blades, and as the rotor is not power-driven in flight no anti-torque system is necessary. Longitudinal and lateral control are effected by mechanically tilting the rotor plane. A contract for the production of 10,000 U-18s has been signed between Umbaugh and Fairchild.

FIAT MODEL 7002

Country of Origin: Italy.
Type: Seven-seat Utility Helicopter.
Power Plant: One Fiat 4700 turbo-generator rated at 530 e.h.p.
Performance: Maximum speed, 106 m.p.h. at sea level; cruising speed, 84 m.p.h. at sea level; range, 187 mls.; service ceiling, 11,150 ft.
Weights: Empty, 1,320 lb.; normal loaded, 3,080 lb.
Dimensions: Rotor diameter, 39 ft. 4¾ in.; fuselage length, 20 ft. 6 in.; overall height, 9 ft. 5½ in.
Development: The Model 7002 is an extremely unconventional helicopter in which the two-blade main rotor is driven by cold jets, compressed air being supplied by the turbo-generator. Featuring exceptional structural simplicity, the fuselage is built up of light alloy sheets, and the standard cabin layout has dual controls plus two separate passenger seats and a bench seat accommodating a further three passengers. For ambulance duties, the fuselage can accommodate two casualty litters, and two additional litters may be carried externally. Despite the absence of torque reaction, a small, mechanically-driven ducted tail rotor is provided to ensure maximum manœuvrability at low forward speeds.

HILLER MODEL E4

Country of Origin: U.S.A.

Type: Four-seat General-purpose Helicopter.

Power Plant: One Lycoming VO-540-A1A six-cylinder horizontally-opposed engine rated at 305 h.p.

Performance: Maximum speed, 96 m.p.h. at sea level; cruising speed (75% power), 88 m.p.h.; economical cruising speed, 84 m.p.h.; range, 225 mls. at 84 m.p.h.; maximum climb rate, 1,340 ft./min.; vertical climb rate, 820 ft./min.; service ceiling, 14,600 ft.; hovering ceiling (with ground effect), 9,550 ft.

Weights: Empty, 1,760 lb.; loaded, 2,750 lb.

Dimensions: Rotor diameter, 35 ft. 4¾ in.; fuselage length, 29 ft. 10¾ in.; overall height, 9 ft. 9½ in.

Development: The Model E4 is derived from the three-seat Model UH-12E, the principal modification being the insertion of a 25-in. section into the standard UH-12E cockpit to increase accommodation. UH-12E helicopters can easily be converted to E4 configuration. A hydraulic cargo hoist, quick-release cargo sling, and cargo racks similar to those that may be provided for the UH-12E can also be fitted to the E4, and dual Marvel-Schebler carburettors which provide an increase of 15 h.p. are to be a standard installation.

264

KAMAN H-43B HUSKIE

Country of Origin: U.S.A.
Type: Eight-seat Crash Rescue Helicopter.
Power Plant: One Lycoming T53-L-1A free turbine rated at 825 s.h.p.
Performance: Maximum speed, 107 m.p.h. at 6,800 ft.; normal range, 250 mls.; hovering ceiling (in ground effect), 20,000 ft.
Weights: Empty, 5,900 lb.; loaded, 7,100 lb.
Dimensions: Rotor diameter (each), 47 ft.; fuselage length, 25 ft.; overall height, 12 ft. 5 in.
Development: Flown for the first time on December 13, 1958, the H-43B Huskie is a development of the piston-engined five-seat H-43A, and 140 machines of this type have been ordered by the U.S.A.F., deliveries to be completed in 1961. Evolved primarily for the short-range rescue role, the H-43B Huskie has a hoist, litter racks, and a specially designed fire-rescue kit which includes 68 Imp. gal. of foam extinguishing chemical, hose, crowbars, axes, etc. Small aileron-like controls mounted on the rotor blades known as servo-flaps improve stability and make possible more sensitive control. A production H-43B has established an altitude record of 30,100 ft. for helicopters in the 3,850–6,614 lb. weight category.

KAMAN HU2K-1 SEASPRITE

Country of Origin: U.S.A.

Type: Six-seat Utility and Search and Rescue Helicopter.

Power Plant: One General Electric T58-GE-6 free turbine rated at 1,024 s.h.p.

Performance: No details available for publication.

Weights: Empty, 5,052 lb.; loaded, 9,152 lb.

Dimensions: Rotor diameter, 44 ft.; fuselage length, 37 ft.; overall height, 12 ft. 5 in.

Development: Designed to meet U.S. Navy requirements for an all-weather utility helicopter, the HU2K-1 Seasprite was flown for the first time on July 1, 1959, and four prototypes were followed by a pre-production batch of twelve machines, the first of which was completed in January 1960. It is anticipated that, providing fleet trials to take place in 1961 are successful, between 250 and 300 Seasprites will be required by the U.S. Navy. These will be employed primarily for search, rescue, utility and high-speed liaison roles, but the Seasprite is capable of carrying up to thirteen combat troops or four casualty litters and medical attendants. An unusual feature of the Seasprite is its retractable undercarriage.

266

MIL MI-1 MOSKVICH (HARE)

Country of Origin: U.S.S.R.
Type: Four-seat Utility Helicopter.
Power Plant: One Ivchenko AI-26V nine-cylinder radial air-cooled engine rated at 575 h.p.
Performance: Maximum speed, 110 m.p.h. at sea level; maximum cruising speed, 93 m.p.h.; economical cruising speed, 87 m.p.h.; range, 310 mls.; ceiling, 19,685 ft.
Weights: (Approximate) Empty, 3,900 lb.; loaded, 5,000 lb.
Dimensions: Rotor diameter, 32 ft. 7 in.; fuselage length, 39 ft. 8 in.; overall height, 10 ft. 10 in.
Development: The Moskvich is the latest development of the Mi-1 which has been in continuous production for ten years. Developed in 1960, the Moskvich has all-metal rotor blades, hydraulic controls and a noise-insulated cabin. The Mi-1 is manufactured under licence in Poland as the SM-1, a five-seat development with an enlarged forward fuselage being designated S-2, and variants include the Mi-1U dual-control trainer, and the Mi-1NKh multi-purpose version that can be employed for casualty evacuation, an enclosed pannier housing a litter being attached to each fuselage side.

267

MIL MI-6 (HOOK)

Country of Origin: U.S.S.R.

Type: Heavy Transport Helicopter.

Power Plants: Two Soloviev TB-2BM free turbines each rated at 5,500 e.h.p. for five minutes and 4,400 e.h.p. normal maximum continuous rating.

Performance: Approximate maximum speed, 175 m.p.h.; normal range, 300 mls.; service ceiling (maximum payload), 13,500 ft.

Weights: Empty, 45,000 lb.; loaded, 71,000 lb.

Dimensions: Rotor diameter, 114 ft. 10 in.; approximate fuselage length, 122 ft. 6 in.; approximate overall height, 40 ft. 6 in.

Development: The world's largest helicopter, the Mi-6 was designed primarily to meet geological survey requirements in Siberia, these calling for the ability to lift a 24,000-lb. payload to an altitude of 12,000 ft. On April 16, 1959, an Mi-6 lifted 22,050 lb. to 16,045 ft., and 11,025 lb. to 18,045 ft., and on November 21, 1959, an Mi-1 established a new world helicopter speed record for the 100-km. closed-circuit with an average speed of 167·206 m.p.h. A speed of 176·5 m.p.h. was attained on one leg of the course.
268

SIKORSKY H-19D CHICKASAW (S-55)

Country of Origin: U.S.A.

Type: Twelve-seat Utility Helicopter.

Power Plant: One Wright R-1300-3 seven-cylinder radial air-cooled engine rated at 700 h.p.

Performance: Maximum speed, 115 m.p.h. at sea level; cruising speed (65% power), 93 m.p.h.; inclined climb rate, 990 ft./min.; hovering ceiling (in ground effect), 8,600 ft.; range, 400 mls.

Weights: Empty, 5,045 lb.; loaded, 7,500 lb.

Dimensions: Rotor diameter, 53 ft.; fuselage length, 42 ft. 2 in.; overall height, 13 ft. 4 in.

Development: The S-55 helicopter was adopted by the U.S. Army Field Forces as the H-19C and D, by the U.S.A.F. as the H-19A and B, by the U.S. Navy as the HO4S-1 and -2, by the U.S. Coastguard as the HO4S-2G, and by the U.S. Marine Corps as the HRS-1, -2, and -3. Three commercial models were produced; the S-55 with the 600-h.p. Pratt and Whitney R-1340, the S-55A with the 700-h.p. Wright R-1300-3, and the S-55C which was similarly powered to the S-55 but featured the inclined tailboom of the S-55A. Assembled in France under licence by Sud-Aviation for the French armed forces, the S-55 was known as the Elephant Joyeux, and one of these machines is illustrated above.

269

SIKORSKY H-37A MOJAVE (S-56)

Country of Origin: U.S.A.

Type: Heavy Transport Helicopter.

Power Plants: Two Pratt and Whitney R-2800-50 eighteen-cylinder air-cooled radial engines each rated at 1,900 h.p.

Performance: Maximum speed, 130 m.p.h. at sea level; cruising speed, 115 m.p.h.; maximum climb rate, 990 ft./min.; hovering ceiling (out of ground effect), 1,100 ft.; service ceiling, 8,700 ft.; combat radius, 69 mls.

Weights: Empty, 20,690 lb.; normal loaded, 30,188 lb.; maximum loaded, 31,000 lb.

Dimensions: Rotor diameter, 72 ft.; fuselage length, 82 ft. 10 in.; overall height, 22 ft.

Development: The S-56 is employed as an assault transport by the U.S. Marine Corps under the designation HR2S-1, and by the U.S. Army as the H-37A Mojave. The Mojave will carry thirty-six fully-equipped troops, a 105-mm. howitzer and its crew, or three MM-100 jeep-type vehicles. There are clamshell doors in the nose, and vehicles can be driven up a ramp. An experimental model equipped with AN/APS-20E early warning radar in a bulbous chin housing is designated HR2S-1W. The S-56 first flew on October 25, 1955.

SIKORSKY H-34A CHOCTAW (S-58)

Country of Origin: U.S.A.
Type: Transport and General-purpose Helicopter.
Power Plant: One Wright R-1820-84 nine-cylinder air-cooled radial rated at 1,525 h.p.
Performance: Maximum speed, 134 m.p.h. at sea level; cruising speed (67% power), 101 m.p.h.; initial climb rate, 1,075 ft./min.; hovering ceiling (with ground effect), 4,000 ft.; normal range, 225 mls.
Weights: Empty, 7,560 lb.; loaded, 12,700 lb.
Dimensions: Rotor diameter, 56 ft.; fuselage length, 46 ft. 9 in.; overall height, 15 ft. 10 in.
Development: The H-34A Choctaw is the U.S. Army version of the S-58, and is employed as a sixteen-seat transport. In its general-purpose form as used by the U.S. Marine Corps it is designated HUS-1, and U.S. Navy versions include the HSS-1 and HSS-1N, the latter using automatic stabilisation equipment. One HSS-1 helicopter was fitted with a General Electric T-58 shaft turbine as a prototype for the HSS-2. The photograph depicts an S-58 helicopter of the Israeli Defence Force/Air Force, and similar helicopters have been supplied to the Armée de l'Air, the Federal German Wehrmacht, the Argentine Navy, and other air arms.

271

SIKORSKY S-60 SKYCRANE

Country of Origin: U.S.A.

Type: Three-seat Crane Helicopter.

Power Plants: Two Pratt and Whitney R-2800-50 eighteen-cylinder radials each rated at 2,100 h.p.

Performance: Maximum speed (without load), 130 m.p.h. at sea level; economical cruising speed, 115 m.p.h. at 2,000 ft.; range, 265 mls., (with 6,000-lb. payload), 100 mls., (with maximum payload), 23 mls.; maximum climb rate, 1,100 ft./min.; hovering ceiling (in ground effect), 6,800 ft.; service ceiling, 10,800 ft.

Weights: Empty, 19,613 lb.; normal loaded, 31,200 lb.; maximum, 34,500 lb.

Dimensions: Rotor diameter, 72 ft.; fuselage length, 65 ft.; overall height, 21 ft. 8 in.

Development: A piston-engined predecessor of a twin-turbine-powered crane designated S-64, the Skycrane employs the rotors, transmission and power plants of the S-56, and is essentially a structural body for carrying crew, engines, rotors and hoists. The accompanying photograph of the Skycrane shows a detachable passenger pod, but loads of any shape or size within the weight limitation of the machine can be lifted, such as missiles, vehicles, bridges, etc. The S-64 will be generally similar in appearance to the Skycrane.

272

SIKORSKY HSS-2 (S-61)

Country of Origin: U.S.A.

Type: Amphibious Anti-submarine Warfare Helicopter.

Power Plants: Two General Electric T58-GE-8 shaft turbines each rated at 1,250 s.h.p.

Performance: Maximum speed, 117 m.p.h. at sea level; economical cruising speed, 98 m.p.h.; maximum climb rate, 1,620 ft./min.; vertical climb rate, 720 ft./min.; hovering ceiling (out of ground effect), 10,800 ft.

Weights: Empty, 10,854 lb.; maximum loaded, 17,300 lb.

Dimensions: Rotor diameter, 62 ft.; fuselage length, 54 ft. 9 in.; overall height, 15 ft. 4 in.

Development: Several variants of the S-61 helicopter are in production, the first of which, the HSS-2 for the U.S. Navy, was flown for the first time in March 1959. An assault transport version, the S-61C, has been developed for the U.S. Marine Corps as the HR3S-1. Capable of carrying 20–25 fully-equipped troops, the HR3S-1 features a rear-loading ramp. A commercial variant, the S-61L powered by CT-58-100 turbines (commercial versions of the T58-GE-8), will carry 25–28 passengers, and the Chicago Helicopter Airways and Los Angeles Airways have respectively ordered six and five for 1961–62 delivery.

S   273

SIKORSKY S-62

Country of Origin: U.S.A.

Type: Amphibious Commercial Transport Helicopter.

Power Plant: One General Electric T58-GE-6 shaft turbine rated at 1,050 s.h.p.

Performance: Maximum speed, 124 m.p.h. at sea level; maximum cruising speed, 115 m.p.h. at 1,000 ft.; maximum climb rate, 1,380 ft./min.; vertical climb rate, 450 ft./min.; hovering ceiling (out of ground effect), 8,000 ft.; service ceiling, 15,700 ft.; range (full payload and 10% reserves), 270 mls.

Weights: Empty, 4,550 lb.; loaded, 7,500 lb.

Dimensions: Rotor diameter, 53 ft.; fuselage length, 44 ft. 7 in.; overall height, 14 ft. 2 in.

Development: Flown for the first time in May 1958, the S-62 employs many of the well-proven components of the S-55, although possessing an entirely new power system and a new hull design for amphibious operation. The first commercial operator to order the S-62 was Los Angeles Airways, and in airline use the helicopter will carry up to ten passengers with provision for a crew of two. It can be rapidly converted for mail or cargo transportation, and the large freight-loading door of the S-55 is retained. The first S-62 was delivered to Los Angeles Airways in September 1960.

274

SUD-AVIATION SE-3160 ALOUETTE III

Country of Origin: France.
Type: Seven-seat General-purpose Helicopter.
Power Plant: One Turboméca Artouste IIIB turbine derated to 450 s.h.p.
Performance: Maximum cruising speed (at 4,190 lb.), 124 m.p.h. at sea level; economical cruising speed, 111 m.p.h.; hovering ceiling, 9,840 ft.; service ceiling, 13,100 ft.; maximum ceiling, 19,650 ft.; range (1,540-lb. payload), 62 mls., (1,190-lb. payload), 186 mls.; maximum range, 334 mls. at 95 m.p.h.
Weights: Empty, 2,300 lb.; normal loaded, 4,190 lb.; maximum loaded, 4,630 lb.
Development: The SE-3160 Alouette III has been derived from the highly successful SE-3130 Alouette II, 500 of which are being built at a rate of six per month, and which is being employed in twenty-one different countries. The Alouette III, which was first flown in March 1959, differs from its predecessor in having a reinforced transmission system, an enlarged and cleaned up fuselage, and an Artouste IIIB in place of the Artouste II. Two prototypes of the Alouette III have been tested, one of these having made a series of landings on Mont Blanc in 1960, and series production is envisaged for 1962.

275

SUD-AVIATION SE-3200 FRELON

Country of Origin: France.

Type: Heavy Transport and Anti-submarine Warfare Helicopter.

Power Plants: Three Turboméca Turmo IIIB free turbines each rated at 750 s.h.p.

Performance: Maximum speed, 153 m.p.h.; cruising speed, 144 m.p.h.; ceiling (at 15,400 lb.), 12,450 ft.; maximum range, 620 mls.

Weights: Empty, 9,920 lb.; normal loaded, 16,550 lb.; maximum, 17,600 lb.

Dimensions: Rotor diameter, 49 ft. 1½ in.; fuselage length, 48 ft. 10½ in.; overall height, 15 ft. 5 in.

Development: The Frelon is a multi-purpose helicopter capable of undertaking the roles of troop transport (24 fully-equipped troops), casualty evacuation (15 casualty litters and two attendants), anti-submarine warfare, and mine-sweeping. The first of two proto-types was flown on June 10, 1959, and the proposed production model will be powered by 1,000–1,100 s.h.p. Turmo IIIC turbines. During its test programme, the Frelon has flown at 17,150 lb. weight and has carried a slung load of 2,420 lb. In mid-1960, one of the two prototypes was handed over to the Centre d'Essais en Vol for official trials.

276

WESTLAND BELVEDERE

Country of Origin: Great Britain.
Type: Military General-purpose and Transport Helicopter.
Power Plants: Two Napier Gazelle 100 (N.Ga.2) free turbines each rated at 1,650 s.h.p.
Performance: Maximum cruising speed, 138 m.p.h.; economic cruising speed, 115 m.p.h.; maximum climb rate, 1,200 ft./min.; vertical climb rate, 385 ft./min.; hovering ceiling (in ground effect), 7,500 ft.; maximum range (standard tankage), 460 mls., (with auxiliary tankage), 783 mls.
Weights: Empty, 11,085 lb.; normal loaded, 18,500 lb.; overload, 20,000 lb.
Dimensions: Rotor diameter (each), 48 ft. 11 in.; fuselage length, 54 ft. 4 in.; overall height, 17 ft. 3 in.
Development: Previously known as the Bristol 192, the Belvedere was flown for the first time on July 5, 1958, and the first three of an order for thirty for the R.A.F. were delivered in September 1960. As a troop transport, the Belvedere can accommodate nineteen fully-equipped troops. For the casualty evacuation role it can accommodate twelve casualty litters and three sitting wounded, and as a freighter up to 6,000 lb. can be carried internally or externally.

WESTLAND ROTODYNE

Country of Origin: Great Britain.
Type: Vertical Take-off and Landing Transport (65 passengers).
Power Plants: Two Rolls-Royce Tyne two-spool turbo-props each rated at 5,250 s.h.p.
Performance: Cruising speed, 200–230 m.p.h. at 5,000 ft.; maximum range, 700 mls. at 200 m.p.h.; vertical climb rate, 2,150 ft./min.; hovering ceiling, 9,000 ft.
Weights: Empty, 35,000 lb.; normal loaded, 53,500 lb.; maximum, 60,000 lb.
Dimensions: Rotor diameter, 109 ft.; wing span, 75 ft.; fuselage length, 69 ft. 5 in.; overall height, 27 ft. 3 in.
Development: The Rotodyne is unique in combining the attributes of a fixed-wing airliner and helicopter, and the Fairey-built prototype (illustrated) powered by 3,000 e.h.p. Napier Eland N.El.3 turboprops had made over 300 flights by the end of 1960 when detail design of the larger, Tyne-powered production model (to which the above specification relates) was well advanced. It is hoped that a C. of A. for the Rotodyne will be obtained by 1965, and Westland is offering a version of the Rotodyne to meet an R.A.F. requirement for a 60-seat V.T.O.L. troop transport.

WESTLAND P.531-2 SCOUT

Country of Origin: Great Britain.
Type: Five/six-seat Light Utility Helicopter.
Power Plant: One Blackburn A.129 Nimbus free turbine engine derated to 650 s.h.p.
Performance: Maximum speed, 127 m.p.h.; maximum cruising speed, 121 m.p.h.; maximum climb rate, 1,490 ft./min.; vertical climb rate, 600 ft./min.; hover ceiling (in ground effect), 17,800 ft.; maximum range (pilot and three passengers plus 10% reserves), 250 mls.
Weights: Empty, 2,836 lb.; normal loaded, 5,000 lb.
Dimensions: Rotor diameter, 32 ft. 3 in.; fuselage length, 30 ft. 10 in.; height, 8 ft. 10 in.
Development: The Scout and the Wasp are respectively civil and military versions of the original Saunders-Roe P.531 which first flew on July 20, 1958. The Wasp differs primarily in having a de Havilland Gnome derated to 650 s.h.p., and the details given above are equally applicable to both types. A contract for the development of the Nimbus-powered Scout was awarded during 1960, and the first pre-production machine for evaluation by the Army flew on August 4, 1960. Three P.531 Mk. 0 aircraft powered by the Blackburn Turmo have been evaluated by the Navy.

279

WESTLAND WESSEX H.A.S.1

Country of Origin: Great Britain.
Type: Anti-submarine Warfare Helicopter.
Power Plant: One Napier Gazelle 160 (N.Ga.13) free turbine rated at 1,450 s.h.p.
Performance: Maximum speed, 132 m.p.h.; maximum cruising speed, 127 m.p.h.; economic cruising speed, 115 m.p.h.; maximum climb rate, 1,750 ft./min.; vertical climb rate, 750 ft./min.; vertical climb rate, 750 ft./min.; hovering ceiling, 7,000 ft.; service ceiling, 14,200 ft.; maximum range, 390 mls.
Weights: Empty, 7,600 lb.; loaded, 12,600 lb.
Dimensions: Rotor diameter, 56 ft.; fuselage length, 49 ft. 11 in.; overall height, 14 ft. 3 in.
Development: Currently entering service with the Royal Navy for submarine detection and strike, the Wessex has been derived from the Sikorsky S-58, and the first prototype machine was flown on June 20, 1958. A Mk. 2 Wessex powered by two 1,250 s.h.p. de Havilland Gnome H.1200 free turbines is under development. Intended for both military and civil roles, this variant will carry sixteen troops as a military transport, as will also the H.A.S.1.

WESTLAND WESTMINSTER

Country of Origin: Great Britain.
Type: Flying Crane or Transport Helicopter (40 passengers).
Power Plants: Two Napier El and E.229A shaft turbines each rated at 2,650 s.h.p.
Performance: Maximum speed, 155 m.p.h.; maximum cruising speed, 150 m.p.h.; economic cruising speed, 115 m.p.h.; maximum climb rate, 2,350 ft./min.; hovering ceiling (out of ground effect), 9,000 ft.; maximum range, 230 mls.
Weights: Basic, 21,345 lb.; loaded, 33,000 lb.
Dimensions: Rotor diameter, 72 ft.; fuselage length, 71 ft. 4 in.; overall height, 18 ft. 4 in.
Development: The Westminster employs the Sikorsky S-56 rotor head and transmission systems, and two prototypes have been built, these flying for the first time on June 15, 1958, and September 4, 1959, respectively. As initially flown, both Westminsters were stripped " flying cranes ", but the first prototype received a faired fuselage in 1960, flying in this form for the first time on June 12th of that year. With its fabric skinning, the first prototype Westminster represents the outline of a possible 40-seat transport. Development of the Westminster has been temporarily suspended.

WESTLAND WHIRLWIND H.A.R.10

Country of Origin: Great Britain.
Type: Ten-seat General-purpose Helicopter.
Power Plant: One de Havilland Gnome H.1000 free turbine rated at 1,050 s.h.p.
Performance: Maximum speed, 109 m.p.h.; maximum economical cruising speed, 104 m.p.h.; maximum climb rate, 1,200 ft./min.; vertical climb rate, 230 ft./min.; hovering ceiling, 14,500 ft.; service ceiling, 15,200 ft.; maximum range (standard tankage), 282 mls.
Weights: Empty, 4,694 lb.; normal loaded, 8,000 lb.
Dimensions: Rotor diameter, 53 ft.; fuselage length, 44 ft. 2 in.; overall height, 15 ft. 7½ in.
Development: Derived from the piston-engined Whirlwind (a licence-built development of the Sikorsky S-55), the Gnome-powered W.A.5 Whirlwind flew for the first time on February 28, 1959, and has been ordered into production for the R.A.F. as the Whirlwind H.A.R.10. The R.A.F. also proposes to convert its piston-engined Whirlwinds to H.A.R.10 standards. The third Gnome-powered machine is truly representative of the H.A.R.10. As a freighter it can carry up to 2,000 lb. of freight, and for casualty evacuation it carries six litters internally.

282

YAKOVLEV YAK-24 (HORSE)

Country of Origin: U.S.S.R.
Type: Military and Commercial Heavy Transport Helicopter.
Power Plants: Two Shvetsov ASh-82V fourteen-cylinder air-cooled radials each rated at 1,700 h.p.
Performance: Maximum speed, 138 m.p.h.; cruising speed, 112 m.p.h.; hovering ceiling (with ground effect) at 35,274 lb., 13,450 ft.; range (at 35,274 lb.), 155 mls., (at 38,590 lb.), 351 mls.; maximum range, 1,056 mls.
Weights: Normal loaded, 35,274 lb.; maximum loaded, 38,590 lb.
Dimensions: Rotor diameter (each), 65 ft. 7½ in.; approximate fuselage length, 80 ft.; approximate overall height, 21 ft.
Development: The Yak-24 entered production for the Soviet Air Forces in 1954, the initial production model being capable of accommodating forty troops, eighteen casualty litters or three M-20 Pobyeda staff cars. Several commercial models have been developed, the latest of which, the Yak-24K, appeared in 1959. Evolved by I. A. Erlikh, the Yak-24K has a shorter fuselage (69 ft.) and is a nine-passenger luxury touring model.

283

INDEX OF AIRCRAFT TYPES

INDEX OF AIRCRAFT TYPES